VITAL SIGNS

2009

ISBN: 978-1-878071-89-7 (13)

Worldwatch Institute
1776 Massachusetts Avenue, NW
Suite 800
Washington, DC 20036
U.S.A.

This book is printed on paper 50% recycled, including 25% post-consumer waste, FSC certified, and elemental chlorine-free.

VITAL SIGNS

2009

The Trends That Are Shaping Our Future

WORLDWATCH INSTITUTE

Alice McKeown, *Project Director*

Erik Assadourian
Zoë Chafe
Amanda Chiu
Hannah Doherty
Robert Engelman
Gary Gardner
Brian Halweil

Petra Löw
Joe Monfort
Michael Renner
Jim Riccio
James Russell
Janet Sawin
Nathan Swire

Linda Starke, *Editor*
Lyle Rosbotham, *Designer*

WITHDRAWN

Worldwatch Institute, Washington, DC

Contents

TECHNICAL NOTE

Units of measure throughout this book are metric unless common usage dictates otherwise. Historical population data used in per capita calculations are from the Center for International Research at the U.S. Bureau of the Census unless noted otherwise. Historical data series in *Vital Signs* are updated in each edition, incorporating any revisions by originating organizations. Unless noted otherwise, references to regions or groupings of countries follow definitions of the Statistics Division of the U.N. Department of Economic and Social Affairs. Data expressed in U.S. dollars have for the most part been deflated (see Notes section for specific details for each trend).

Acknowledgments

Since its launch in the early 1990s, *Vital Signs* has become a mainstay of Worldwatch Institute's work, allowing us to track and explain the most important environmental, economic, and social trends of our time. In addition to capturing how the world's economies and societies are changing, these trends highlight leverage points for building a more sustainable society.

We are pleased to offer this new *Vital Signs* edition—a compilation of 25 trends we tracked on our website over the last year—in one convenient reference guide. We hope this book becomes as important a part of your library as the other quality Worldwatch reports you have come to expect, including our flagship annual *State of the World*.

Over the past two years, we have worked to recreate *Vital Signs* and to make the trends as relevant as possible, both to leading decisionmakers and to everyday citizens. We are eagerly anticipating the launch of our new subscription-based *Vital Signs Online* service, which will provide convenient online access to the analysis, endnotes, datasets, and presentation-ready graphs for each trend throughout the year. We hope you will come to depend on this service as a useful tool for work in the boardroom, classroom, or anywhere else.

We have many visionary staff members to thank for *Vital Signs Online*, but special acknowledgment goes to two former project directors, Erik Assadourian and Zoë Chafe. Senior Researcher Gary Gardner has also been a dedicated mentor for *Vital Signs Online*, generously offering his time and skills and helping to bridge staff transitions.

Many things have changed in the more than 15 years since *Vital Signs* was launched, but through it all we have depended on funders who share our commitment to a more sustainable society. We owe particular thanks to the American Clean Skies Foundation, the Heinrich Böll Foundation, the Blue Moon Fund, the Casten Family Foundation, the Compton Foundation, Inc., The Goldman Environmental Prize, the Richard and Rhoda Goldman Fund, the Good Energies Foundation, the Jake Family Fund, the W. K. Kellogg Foundation, the Steven C. Leuthold Family Foundation, the Marianists of the USA Sharing Fund, the Netherlands Environment Ministry, the Norwegian Royal Ministry of Foreign Affairs, the V. Kann Rasmussen Foundation, The Shared Earth Foundation, The Shenandoah Foundation, the Sierra Club, Stonyfield Farm, the TAUPO Fund, the Flora L. Thornton Foundation, the United Nations Population Fund, the United Nations Environment Programme, the Wallace Genetic Foundation, Inc., the Wallace Global Fund, the Johanette Wallerstein Institute, the Winslow Foundation, and the World Wildlife Fund–Europe.

We are also thankful to the more than 3,000 Friends of Worldwatch who fund nearly one third of our operating budget. In addition to financial support, our generous Board of Directors helps us make strategic decisions and donates considerable time to our causes. We are also grateful to our dedicated development staff, including Director of Institutional Relations Mary Redfern and Director of Individual Giving Courtney Berner. Development Assistant Kimberly Rogovin provides unwavering support.

Many of the trends in this volume would not have been possible without the expertise and dedication of our on-staff researchers. In particular, we are thankful for the work of our climate and energy specialists, including Worldwatch President Christopher Flavin and Energy and Climate Change Program Director Janet Sawin.

We are also fortunate to reflect the voices of several outside experts in this edition who served as either authors or peer reviewers. We are thankful for the contributions of Petra Löw of Munich Re for her analysis of weather-related disasters; Joe Monfort for his trends on energy issues; Jim Riccio of Greenpeace USA for his article on nuclear power; and James Russell, a former Worldwatch MAP Sustainable Energy fellow, for his numerous pieces on energy issues. Two summer interns also contributed: Hannah Doherty who wrote a trend on child mortality and Nathan Swire who coauthored a piece on energy-efficient lighting.

No book can come together without the efforts of many people behind the scenes. We are especially grateful for the excellent editing skills of Linda Starke, who has helped finesse Worldwatch publications for more than 25 years. Art Director Lyle Rosbotham elegantly captured the feel of *Vital Signs* while gracefully adapting to our new format and varied trend lengths. Marketing Director Patricia Shyne made publishing this book possible, and Senior Editor Lisa Mastny helped push it over the finish line.

Other Worldwatch staff members contribute daily to our efforts to distribute our research and messages as widely as possible. The communications team, including Darcey Rakestraw, Julia Tier, and Ben Block, works relentlessly to raise awareness of the issues we cover. Tom Prugh, Editor of *World Watch* magazine, serves as a beacon on the latest environmental topics. Our administrative team—Barbara Fallin and Juliane Diamond—gives staff the tools we need to function smoothly.

I hope you enjoy this edition of *Vital Signs* and that these articles help not only to inform but to inspire the changes needed to build a sustainable world.

Alice McKeown
Project Director
Worldwatch Institute
1776 Massachusetts Avenue, N.W.
Washington, DC 20036

Preface

If one word could capture the major sustainability issues of the past year, it would be "crisis": energy crisis, financial crisis, food crisis. As this latest edition of *Vital Signs* illustrates, the roots of these seemingly disparate problems are deep, interconnected, and have been brewing for a long time.

The start of 2008 looked remarkably different from where we ended the year: oil consumption was up, a U.S. presidential contest was under way, and governments around the world were showing new determination to tackle climate change, following the latest reports from the Intergovernmental Panel on Climate Change.

But fast-forward to the end of the year—after oil peaked at an all-time high of $147 a barrel in July—and much of this optimism had crumbled into what is now a devastating global recession. Automobile companies are struggling to stay afloat. Financial scandals abound. And "hypermiling"—the act of maximizing gas mileage through car and driver adjustments—was named the *New American Oxford Dictionary* 2008 word of the year.

The effects of fossil fuels were not felt only at the gas pump in 2008. Estimates of potential sea level rise from climate change went up significantly and are well above previous projections. New observations suggest that the Arctic is releasing large quantities of methane, a potent greenhouse gas. And 2008 was added to the list of 10 warmest years ever, a trend that has repeated itself eight times in the past decade.

As global awareness about climate change grew, climate scientist James Hansen offered a new target for atmospheric concentrations of carbon dioxide—350 parts per million—and quickly won support from the public and scientific community. In the face of this challenging goal, however, the U.S. Congress failed in its first effort to approve climate change legislation, voting down the Lieberman-Warner bill.

But not all of the news was so gloomy. At the G8 meeting in July, leading industrial countries agreed to cut their greenhouse gas emissions by 50 percent. Voters in the United States elected a new administration that appears to be committed to addressing climate change and bringing about a new energy economy. A consortium of European governments announced the creation of the first International Renewable Energy Agency to champion clean energy worldwide.

Even as energy prices soared and the climate warmed, the world was confronted by a food crisis that may well have been exacerbated by those other trends. The year was marked by skyrocketing food prices fueled in part by the rising cost of oil, low cereal stocks, extreme weather events, and subsidies for biofuels that triggered a "food-versus-fuel" debate across much of the world. Although food prices fell along with oil prices late in the year, they remain much higher than four years ago. Already, more than 100 million people worldwide have been driven deeply into poverty by the food crisis, and another year of record prices is likely.

Added to these economic tensions are the ongoing effects of land degradation, which the

United Nations Food and Agriculture Organization warns could put one quarter of the world's population at risk from food insecurity. Climate change, water scarcity, crop losses, and pest infestations may cause forecasted crop yields to be up to 25 percent short of global demand in as little as 40 years.

The trends documented in *Vital Signs* provide the context to better understand these economic and environmental events as they unfold today, and how they have developed over time. They show, for example, that wind power continues to grow at record rates, with a 27 percent increase in 2007. Solar power, starting at a much smaller capacity, was up 51 percent. For the third year in a row, global oil demand grew at an annual rate of less than 2 percent. Coal made up 25 percent of the world primary energy supply, but accounted for 40 percent of carbon dioxide emissions from fossil fuels. Production of ethanol, a biofuel that has developed during the last decade, was up 17 percent in 2007, and biodiesel was up 33 percent.

Globally, at least 2.3 million people work directly in the renewable energy field or indirectly in supplier industries. This labor force is projected to expand with reductions in fossil fuel use and with the growth in renewables, as "green-collar" jobs tend to be more labor-intensive than conventional energy positions. At the same time, the continued rise in carbon emissions—2.8 percent globally in 2007—is likely to displace increasing numbers of people from their homes and livelihoods, especially in low-lying coastal zones, small island states, and areas with already-severe water shortages. Consumer energy habits are also shifting: higher gas prices led to more bicycle commuters, and public bike-rental programs are on the rise.

Grain harvests were up in 2007 after several years of declines. However, the amount of grain stored by governments as a cushion against poor harvests and rising prices continues to decline and was down to 14 percent, the lowest level in 30 years. Meat production—which relies on grain for animal feed—was steady in 2007 but is expected to nearly double by 2050,

to 465 million tons. Much of this demand will be met through factory farms, which are increasingly situated near urban centers and are likely to become a serious public health challenge in the coming years. Livestock are already responsible for 18 percent of human-caused greenhouse gas emissions, more than the share from transportation.

The world's wild fish catch declined for the second year in a row and continues to fall from its peak in 2000. Meanwhile, fish farming is expanding rapidly: aquaculture now outpaces all other animal food sectors, with average annual growth of 8.6 percent in recent decades, compared with 2.8 percent for meat production. Aquaculture trends indicate stronger growth rates in carnivorous fish species such as tuna and salmon, which require higher energy inputs than farmed fish that are lower on the food chain. Genetically modified crops, which have been cast as an agricultural solution for more than a decade, continue to focus on four cash crops yet account for just 9 percent of total land used for primary crop production.

Vital Signs 2009 describes a world with deep ecological debts as well as serious economic problems. But it also demonstrates that the three major sustainability crises facing the world today—energy, food, and economic—are interrelated. On a positive note, it shows that these crises can be addressed by coordinated interventions that work to reverse climate change, jumpstart an energy revolution, and create new economic opportunities. If ever there were a time to stop, think, and create change, that moment is now.

We hope you enjoy this edition of *Vital Signs* and that you will keep up to date on these important trends throughout the year by visiting our new electronic companion series, *Vital Signs Online*. This subscription service, which is being updated continuously, will enable you to track key global trends—and be ready to respond as they unfold.

Alice McKeown
Project Director, Worldwatch Institute

Food and Agriculture Trends

John Byer

Ripening wheat crop

For data and analysis on food and agriculture trends, go to www.worldwatch.org/vsonline.

Grain Harvest Sets Record, But Supplies Still Tight

Brian Halweil

Following several years of declining harvests, the world's farmers reaped a record 2.316 billion tons of grain in 2007.[1] (See Figure 1.) Despite this jump of 95 million tons, or about 4 percent, over the previous year, commodity analysts estimate that voracious global demand will consume all of this increase and prevent governments from replenishing cereal stocks that are at their lowest level in 30 years.[2]

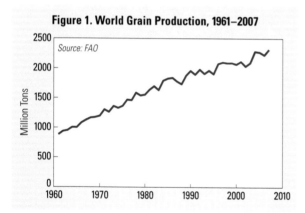

Figure 1. World Grain Production, 1961–2007

Source: FAO

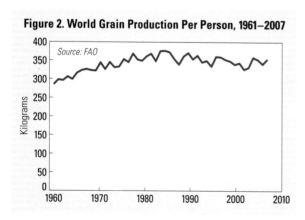

Figure 2. World Grain Production Per Person, 1961–2007

Source: FAO

The global grain harvest has nearly tripled since 1961, during a time when world population doubled.[3] As a result, the amount of grain produced per person grew from 285 kilograms in 1961 to a peak of 376 kilograms in 1986.[4] (See Figure 2.) In recent decades, as the growth in grain production has matched population growth, per capita production has hovered around 350 kilograms.[5]

But output per person varies dramatically by region. For instance, it stands at roughly 1,230 kilograms per year in the United States, most of which is fed to livestock, compared with 325 kilograms in China and just 90 kilograms in Zimbabwe.[6]

Economists, hunger activists, and agricultural researchers track world grain production because people still primarily eat foods made from grain. On average, humans get about 48 percent of their calories from grains, a share that has declined just slightly, from 50 percent, over the last four decades.[7] Grains, particularly corn, in conjunction with soybeans, also form the primary feedstock for industrial livestock production.

People consume a little less than half (48 percent) of the world's grain directly—as steamed rice, bread, tortillas, or millet cakes, for instance.[8] Roughly one third (35 percent) becomes livestock feed.[9] And a growing share, 17 percent, is used to make ethanol and other fuels.[10]

Although high crop prices have been pushing farmers around the world to plant more land in grains in recent years, a more powerful engine for the record output was a boost in average yields, the amount of grain harvested per hectare. For the last decade, grain yields have surpassed 3 tons—nearly three times the level in 1960.[11] Near-perfect weather in major growing areas as well as an estimated 5 percent jump in world fertilizer use helped farmers increase yields.[12]

World grain production is concentrated in a number of ways—in terms of the species produced, where the crops are raised, and the major exporters. Corn, wheat, and rice account for about 85 percent of the global grain harvest (in terms of weight), with sorghum, millet, barley, oats, and other less common grains rounding out the total.[13]

China, India, and the United States alone account for 46 percent of global grain production; Europe, including the former Soviet states, grows another 21 percent.[14] Argentina, Australia, Canada, the European Union (EU), and the United States account for 80 percent of wheat exports, while just three nations—Argentina, the EU, and the United States—account for 80 percent of corn exports.[15]

In 2007, a 200-million-ton jump in the global coarse grain harvest was responsible for nearly all of the increase in the total grain harvest.[16] Production of coarse grains—a group that includes corn, barley, sorghum, and other grains fed mainly to animals—increased 10 percent, from 985 million tons in 2006 to 1,080 million tons in 2007.[17] At 784 million tons, the record harvest of corn was buoyed by the growing use of this grain to produce biofuels, which prompted farmers in the United States (responsible for over 40 percent of the global harvest and half of world exports), Brazil, and Argentina to plant more land to corn.[18] Production in China, the world's second largest corn producer, inched beyond the previous year's record.[19]

Worldwide, the amount of coarse grains converted to energy jumped 15 percent to 255 million tons, although this is still small compared with the 627 million tons devoted to another relatively inefficient use—livestock feed.[20]

Wheat harvests increased modestly, by 2 percent, to 605 million tons, with near perfect weather nurturing strong harvests in India, the EU, and the United States.[21] Australia, however, normally the source of one third of world exports, faced lower crop prospects and depleted exportable supplies.[22] And unfavorable weather meant a reduced harvest in China, the world's second largest producer.[23]

The global rice harvest was up slightly to 633 million tons, matching the record 2005 harvest, as conditions returned to normal in China, India, and across Asia, which accounts for 90 percent of world production.[24]

The amount of grain stored by governments—a good measure of the global cushion against poor harvests and rising prices—continues to decline. Global cereal stocks were expected to stand at 318 million tons by the close of the 2007 season, equivalent to about 14 percent of annual consumption.[25] (See Figure 3.) These stocks, and the stock-to-use ratio, built up by bumper crops in the 1980s and the late 1990s, are now substantially below their all-time high.[26]

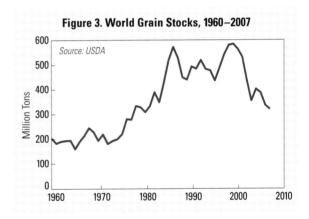

Figure 3. World Grain Stocks, 1960–2007

Source: USDA

Despite the record harvest, the low stocks and strong demand combined to push prices of all cereals to new highs.[27] At harvest time, the U.S. corn export price was up about 70 percent from the previous year, while the American hard wheat price averaged 65 percent more than a year earlier.[28] Wheat prices in Argentina, another major exporter, doubled since 2006.[29] Important wheat exporters like Ukraine and Russia have imposed export restrictions to ensure a sufficient domestic supply.[30] Major importers, like Egypt, the European Union,

Yemen, and Iraq, have reacted to high prices by purchasing grain early, which has further tightened supplies and boosted prices.[31]

As such increases ripple through the food chain, people around the world have been greeted with higher prices for bread, beer, corn flour, and other basic foods. Developing countries are likely to spend a record $52 billion on imports of cereals in 2007, up 10 percent from 2006.[32] This follows a 36-percent hike in the previous season.[33]

Even international food aid programs, which also purchase their supplies on the world mar-

ket, have been forced to scale back.[34] The volume of aid provided through the largest assistance program in the United States, Food for Peace, dropped by nearly half since 2005, to 2.4 million tons, in response to a 35-percent increase in the cost of agricultural commodities as well as the rising costs of fuel for shipping.[35] The combination of rising food costs and declining aid can be fatal for the estimated 854 million people worldwide who experience hunger on a regular basis.[36]

Meat Production Continues to Rise

Brian Halweil

In 2007, meat production remained steady at an estimated 275 million tons; in 2008, output is expected to top 280 million tons.[1] (See Figure 1.) Experts predict that by 2050 nearly twice as much meat will be produced as today, for a projected total of more than 465 million tons.[2] For more than a decade, the strongest increases in production have been in the developing world—in 1995 more meat and dairy products were produced in developing than in industrial countries for the first time, and this trend has continued ever since.[3] In fact, in 2007 at least 60 percent of meat was produced in developing nations.[4]

Consumption of meat and other animal products also continues to grow. Currently nearly 42 kilograms of meat is produced per person worldwide, but meat consumption varies greatly by region and socioeconomic status.[5] In the developing world, people eat about 30 kilograms of meat a year.[6] But consumers in the industrial world eat more than 80 kilograms per person each year.[7] (See Figure 2.)

Rising food prices are pushing consumers to choose cheaper cuts of meat, like chicken. (See Figure 3.) Global poultry output in 2007 was expected to reach 93 million tons, a 4-percent increase from the previous year.[8] The United States is the biggest poultry producer, but other major producers, including Argentina, Brazil, China, the Philippines, and Thailand, are all expecting increases in production. India, however, is likely to have lower poultry production because of the spread of the H5N1 avian flu virus and the culling of millions of chickens.[9]

Pig meat production in 2007 was expected to rise nearly 2 percent, to 101 million tons.[10] It declined the previous year as a result of Porcine Reproductive and Respiratory Disease in China and the massive culling of at least 1 million pigs.[11] China, however, continues to be the world's largest producer of pig meat, although production is expanding in South America. Argentina, Brazil, and Chile are all increasing pig production, thanks to ample supplies of feed.[12]

Beef output rose by 2.3 percent, with nearly 67 million tons produced in 2007.[13] The United

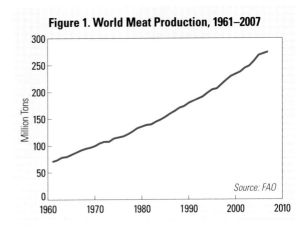

Figure 1. World Meat Production, 1961–2007

Source: FAO

Figure 2. Meat Production Per Person, World, Industrial, and Developing Countries, 1961–2007

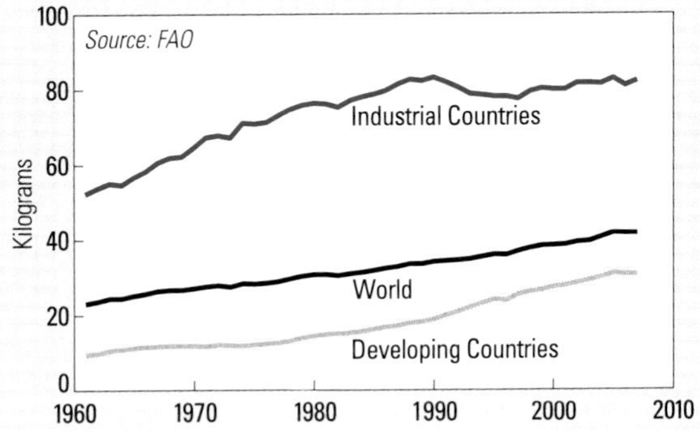

Source: FAO

States is still the world's largest beef producer, but 56 percent of production now takes place in the developing world.[14] China's beef production is expected to grow by 3 percent in 2008, and despite traditional religious beliefs about the sacredness of cows, India, along with Pakistan, is responding to growing consumer demand for more-western diets by increasing beef production and slaughter.[15]

Much of the growing demand for animal

Figure 3. World Meat Production by Source, 2007

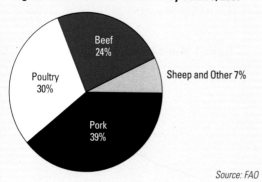

Beef
24%

Poultry
30%

Sheep and Other 7%

Pork
39%

Source: FAO

products worldwide is being met by concentrated animal feeding operations, or factory farms.[16] Worldwide, some 56 billion animals are raised and slaughtered for food each year.[17] Factory farms account for 67 percent of poultry meat production, 50 percent of egg production, and 42 percent of pork production.[18] These facilities rely on commercial breeds of livestock, usually pigs and chickens, that have been bred to gain weight quickly on high-protein feeds. Factory farms are also very crowded, confining animals closely together—many of the world's 17 billion hens and meat chickens each live in an area that is less than the size of a sheet of paper.[19] Cattle in feedlots often stand knee-high in manure and arrive at slaughterhouses covered in feces.[20]

In addition, such operations are increasingly located in or near cities in the developing world, making urban areas the center of industrial meat

production in some countries. And while city dwellers have kept livestock privately for centuries to help dispose of some urban waste, as well as a source of income and food, large industrial operations can create a host of environmental and public health problems. According to the World Bank, the "extraordinary proximate concentration of people and livestock poses probably one of the most serious environmental and public health challenges for the coming decades."[21] Diseases such as avian flu, pig fever, and Nipah virus can all spread very quickly among animals living in confined animal feeding operations because of the crowded and filthy conditions. BSE, or mad cow disease, was likely the result of feeding cattle the ground-up bits of other ruminants.[22] And the use of antibiotics in factory farming is leading to antibiotic resistance.[23] In the United States, livestock now consume 70 percent of all antimicrobial drugs.[24]

Livestock are also responsible for 18 percent of greenhouse gas (GHG) emissions, as measured in carbon dioxide equivalent, which is higher than the share of GHG emissions from transportation.[25] They produce 37 percent of methane, which has more than 20 times the global warming potential of carbon dioxide, and they emit 65 percent of nitrous oxide, another powerful GHG, most of which comes from manure.[26]

Another environmental problem is water use: livestock operations are major water users and polluters. The irrigation of feed crops for cattle accounts for nearly 8 percent of global human water use.[27] The large amount of waste produced on factory farms exceeds the capacity of nearby cropland to absorb it. As a result, manure goes from being a valuable agricultural resource to what is essentially toxic waste. Nitrates, heavy metals, and antibiotics present in manure can seep into groundwater and pollute surface water, threatening public health.[28]

One way to prevent some of these problems is to discourage large producers from keeping animals in or near cities. A combination of zoning and land use regulations, taxes, incentives, and infrastructure development can encourage them to raise animals closer to croplands, where manure can be used as fertilizer and where there is less risk of disease transmission to people. Controlling land and livestock nutrient imbalances means raising livestock in areas that have enough land to handle the waste from large operations. Thailand, for example, has levied high taxes on poultry production within a 100-kilometer radius of Bangkok.[29] As a result, over the last decade poultry production near Bangkok has dropped significantly.[30]

Consumers will need to rethink the place of meat and other animal products in their diets to promote better human and environmental health. A recent article, for example, in the *European Journal of Clinical Nutrition* notes that "vegetarian and vegan diets could play an important role in preserving environmental resources and in reducing hunger and malnutrition in poorer nations."[31] And the authors of a September 2007 article in the highly respected medical journal *The Lancet* recommended that people in the industrial world eat 10 percent less meat as a way to reduce greenhouse gas emissions as well as improve human health: "The unprecedented serious challenge posed by climate change necessitates radical responses.... For the world's higher-income populations, greenhouse-gas emissions from meat-eating warrant the same scrutiny as do those from driving and flying."[32]

Genetically Modified Crops Only a Fraction of Primary Global Crop Production

Alice McKeown

In 2007, farmers planted an additional 12.3 million hectares of genetically modified (GM) crops, bringing the total global area up 12 percent to 114.3 million hectares.[1] (See Figure 1.) Genetically modified crops (also called biotech crops) have been intentionally altered through genetic engineering—the elimination, alteration, or introduction of new genetic elements, including from one unrelated species to another. Although they have been on the market for a decade, they currently account for a modest 9 percent of total land used for global primary crops.[2] (See Figure 2.) Four cash crops continue to account for virtually all GM production: soybean (51 percent), corn (31 percent), cotton (13 percent), and canola (5 percent).[3]

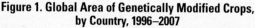
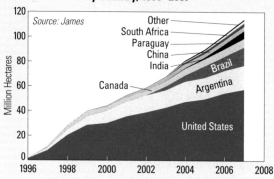

Figure 1. Global Area of Genetically Modified Crops, by Country, 1996–2007

Source: James

Other
South Africa
Paraguay
China
India
Brazil
Canada
Argentina
United States

Million Hectares

120
100
80
60
40
20
0

1996 1998 2000 2002 2004 2006 2008

Twenty-three countries were growing GM crops in 2007, including 17 high-income and upper-middle-income countries and 6 lower-middle-income countries.[4] The global leader by far continues to be the United States, which accounts for half of all GM crop area.[5] In 2007, GM crops were growing on 57.7 million hectares of U.S. land, an increase of 6 percent over the previous year.[6] Beyond the four standard GM crops, farmers there also grew small amounts of GM papaya in Hawaii, although that has been declining over the past few years, and GM alfalfa, which court rulings have suspended until further environmental review.[7]

The second and third largest countries for GM crop area are Argentina, with 19.1 million hectares in 2007, and Brazil, with 15.0 million hectares.[8] Other primary South American growers include Paraguay with 2.6 million hectares and Uruguay with 500,000 hectares.[9] The main GM crop grown in this region is soybeans, followed by corn and cotton.[10]

India is now ranked fifth in total GM crop area, with 6.2 million hectares in 2007 devoted to cotton.[11] This includes 2.4 million hectares that were planted between 2006 and 2007, about the same amount of new area as added the previous year. Although China was the first country to grow a commercial genetically modified crop—transgenic tobacco in 1992—added crop area rates there have significantly trailed those of India.[12] In 2007 China had 3.8 million hectares in GM crops, including 300,000 new hectares, about one eighth as much as India's new crop area for the same year.[13] The main GM crop in China is cotton.[14]

Two GM crop traits continue to dominate worldwide: herbicide tolerance (63 percent) and insect resistance (18 percent), with a combination of the two traits (called "stacked") accounting for the rest.[15] (See Figure 3.) For herbicides, most crops have been altered to tolerate direct application of glyphosate, commonly known by the trade name Roundup.[16] While GM crops adopted during the initial years of commercialization were mostly single-trait crops, the recent trend has been for stacked traits that are a combination of herbicide tolerance and insect resistance.[17] This trend has been most prevalent over the last four years, as stacked crops grew from 9 percent to 19 percent of traits.[18]

In the United States, GM crop production actually increased pesticide use by more than 4 percent between 1996 and 2004, despite early signs that GM use might be tied to an overall decline.[19] Reports of glyphosate-resistant weeds, or "super weeds," have been on the rise since GM crops started gaining momentum, and these weeds now total 15 species—up from 2 in the 1990s—that cover hundreds of thousands of hectares in the United States alone.[20] In response, farmers have been encouraged to diversify herbicide applications or increase glyphosate applications.[21]

Claims of potential benefits from GM crops include increased yields and nutritional value, although to date no commercially available crops have been modified for these purposes.[22] Some studies have shown that GM crops reduce yield performance, including a 5- to 10-percent yield drag in GM soybeans.[23] Media reports have linked the widespread collapse of GM cotton crops and reduced yields in India to increased suicides among poor farmers.[24] And although nutrition-related traits have been promised over the last decade, they are still at least five years away from market.[25]

Several concerns surround GM crops, including the transfer of food allergens across crop species, the unintentional spread and gene flow of GM crops, contamination of organic and other non-GM crops, the development of weed and pest resistance, and toxicity to animals that may feed on or near the crops.[26] One social concern is the use of genetic use restriction technologies (GURTs), which can prevent the appearance of a GM trait or cause the seeds to be sterile in order to keep GM crops from being replicated or saved and replanted by farmers for the next crop.[27] Sometimes called "terminator seeds," GURTs pose environmental risks and have been restricted, although research into new varieties continues.[28]

The potential social benefits of GM crops

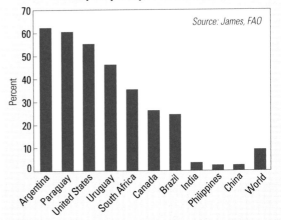

Figure 2. Genetically Modified Crops as Share of Primary Crops, Top 10 Countries, 2007

Source: James, FAO

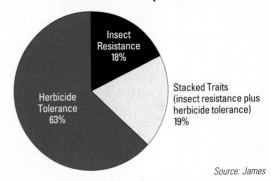

Figure 3. Genetically Modified Crop Traits, Share of Global Crop Area, 2007

Insect Resistance 18%

Herbicide Tolerance 63%

Stacked Traits (insect resistance plus herbicide tolerance) 19%

Source: James

for small farmers and consumers in developing countries have not yet been realized in part because large profit-driven agribusinesses have dominated research and development and hold intellectual property protections that make public research costly and time-consuming.[29] In addition, most investment has been into a small number of crops and traits targeted toward large-scale commercial farming.[30]

The Food and Agriculture Organization has warned of a growing "molecular divide" between industrial and developing countries, advocating a new direction that would address the needs of the poor, including research into so-called orphan crops—sorghum, millet, and pigeon pea, among others—that have received little or no attention.[31] Other critics maintain that GM research threatens local agricultural knowledge and experimentation, two important components of a sustainable agricultural system.[32] These concerns raise questions about portraying GM crops as a second Green Revolution: whereas in the Green Revolution research was driven by public centers and focused on providing free technology and access to those most in need, the "Gene Revolution" is largely being driven by commercial profits.[33]

Monsanto exemplifies the growing influence of GM agribusinesses and seed companies: its GM crop traits are found in more than 85 percent of global GM crop hectares, and the company controls 23 percent of the global proprietary seed market.[34] Monsanto has been a leading proponent of prohibiting farmers from saving seeds to plant as future crops, increasing the dependence of farmers on seed companies.[35] The company has collected tens of millions of dollars from farmers charged with illegally saving GM seed, even in cases where accidental contamination was the likely culprit.[36]

Rising food prices worldwide have led to increased media attention on GM crops. In early 2008, GM proponents like Monsanto began promoting their technology as part of the global solution to an impending food crisis, even though there are no GM crops available to increase yields.[37] Livestock producers and feed makers joined the media fray, urging faster approval of GM crops and more widespread use of the technology.[38] Yet a groundbreaking report by more than 400 scientists published in April 2008 and approved by more than 50 countries casts serious doubts about the role of GM crops in addressing food security and points to the existence of more-effective alternatives and solutions.[39]

Another area that is gaining attention is the overlap of GM crops and climate change. Some proponents have highlighted the use of GM crops in biofuels production, including 7 million hectares of corn used in ethanol and just over 4 million hectares of soybeans used in biodiesel.[40] But there are no commercially available GM crops designed for biofuels, which are made equally well from conventional crops. Moreover, biofuels may result in higher lifecycle greenhouse gas emissions than conventional petroleum fuels.[41]

Also receiving attention are crops that may be able to adapt to changing climate conditions like drought and extreme temperatures—sometimes called "climate-ready."[42] Several large agribusinesses have announced significant research investments into these crops, including one partnership with nonprofit and research groups, called Water Efficient Maize for Africa, to develop drought-tolerant corn.[43] However, there are many substantial technical obstacles to successful development of these traits through genetic modification.[44] Like earlier promises of higher nutrition, most of the "climate-ready" GM crops are not expected to be widely available for 5–10 years even if they turn out to be viable.[45]

Even as these developments advance, tension is growing over the future of GM crops. The European Union is expected to offer new guidance on these crops by the end of 2008, a process that has already proved controversial, with allegations of secret meetings to sway the decision.[46] France announced earlier this year that it was suspending GM crop production, but two other countries are expected to join the mix by the end of 2008: Egypt and Burkina Faso.[47] New crops are also in development, including rice—one of the most important food staples for a majority of the world's poor.[48] Yet a new scientific study funded by the Austrian government suggests that a popular variety of GM corn reduces fertility in mice, raising questions about GM safety.[49] And with high-level critics like the Prince of Wales speaking out, GM crops are likely to remain controversial.[50]

Fish Farming Continues to Grow as World Fisheries Stagnate

Alice McKeown and Brian Halweil

World seafood production neared 160 million tons in 2006, the last year for which there are data.[1] (See Figure 1.) The growth over the previous year was entirely due to increased fish farming, or aquaculture, which increased by more than 3 million tons, an annual addition that has been fairly consistent over the last 10 years.[2] In contrast, fish caught in the wild declined for the second year in a row and dropped to almost 4 million tons below the peak catch in 2000.[3]

About 75 percent of the fish caught and produced each year are destined for human consumption.[4] This adds up to about 16.5 kilograms of fish per person annually on a global scale.[5] In 2004, more than 2.6 billion people depended on fish for at least 20 percent of their animal protein.[6]

People in China eat the most fish, with an average 25.8 kilograms live weight equivalent per person, compared with a figure of only 8.2 kilograms in Africa.[7] People in North and Central America eat 18.6 kilograms, while Europeans consume 19.9 kilograms a year.[8] Not surprisingly, people who live in coastal areas eat more fish than others in the same country or region; in Oceania, per capita consumption is 23.5 kilograms.[9] Differences within continents are also common: in the United States, the average fish consumption is 24.2 kilograms while in Mexico it is 11.6 kilograms; in Spain, the figure is 42.9 kilograms, compared with 34.3 kilograms in France, 29.5 kilograms in Sweden, and 19.8 kilograms in the United Kingdom.[10]

Globally, total seafood production grew at a slower rate than meat output for 8 of the last 10 years.[11] But aquaculture growth continues to far outpace all other animal food sectors, with average annual rates of 8.6 percent over three decades, compared with 2.8 percent for meat production during the same period.[12] Projec-

tions indicate that seafood demand will continue to grow along with population and incomes, especially as people in developing countries increase their overall consumption of animal products.[13]

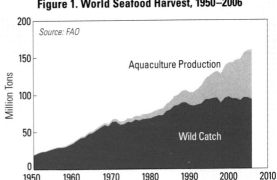

Figure 1. World Seafood Harvest, 1950–2006

Source: FAO

The world's fisheries have remained relatively stable over the last 15 years: about 50 percent are being fished at full capacity, 25 percent are underfished, and the remainder are overexploited, depleted, or recovering.[14] As a result, the U.N. Food and Agriculture Organization predicts that maximum wild fish capture has already been reached.[15] Most of the stocks of the top 10 fished species are being fully fished or are overexploited, and studies have indicated that even in the most stable fisheries there have been declines in the most valuable species, such as tuna.[16]

Asia and the Pacific region dominate global aquaculture production, accounting for more than 90 percent.[17] China is by far the world leader, with more than 45 million tons produced in 2006—about 70 percent of global output and more than half of the total global value from aquaculture.[18] The next closest producer is India, with just over 3 million tons.[19] The only country outside this region in the top 10 producing countries is Chile.[20] (See Figure 2.)

At the same time that wild marine catches face further decline or stagnation, aquaculture production offers further growth potential. In China, more than three quarters of the fish supply comes from aquaculture, while the average for the rest of the world is 20 percent and rising.[21] Sub-Saharan countries in Africa have the largest untapped potential because of resources like clean water and unused land.[22]

Historically, most of the world's aquaculture has focused on species that are relatively low on the food chain, including seaweeds, shellfish, and herbivorous or omnivorous species like carp.[23] However, recent trends indicate stronger growth rates in carnivorous species like shrimp and salmon will continue, especially as demand increases.[24] (See Figure 3.)

Due in part to this trend, growth in aquaculture now drives global fishmeal and fish oil production. Until recently, fishmeal and fish oil were used primarily for pig and poultry production; today nearly 50 percent of fishmeal and 87 percent of fish oil is used in aquaculture.[25] In 1948, only 7.7 percent of wild-caught fish were reduced to fishmeal or fish oil, but that number has grown to 37 percent.[26] Because fishmeal and fish oil depend on overly taxed marine fisheries, increasing production on a large scale is unlikely.[27]

Increasing the use of fishmeal and fish oil in aquaculture raises health and environmental concerns. The rendering process used to prepare these products concentrates the toxins found in the fish, including carcinogenic dioxins, which accumulate up through the food chain to people who eat contaminated fish.[28] This problem is seen clearly in farmed salmon, which consistently have significantly higher levels of dioxin than their wild counterparts.[29] Another troublesome toxin that accumulates in fish is mercury, which is especially dangerous for children.[30]

Dependence on rendered fish also decreases the efficiency of farming fish, as fish-derived feed products require more energy to produce than plant-based ones.[31] For farmed salmon, as much as 90 percent of all energy inputs go into providing food for the salmon.[32] Indeed, farmed salmon can require five times more energy per edible protein unit than farmed shellfish.[33]

Fish farms themselves, especially ones that raise carnivorous fish, can be a large source of water pollution, including nitrogen and excess nutrients that can create toxic blooms and dead zones.[34] Because fish are often raised in high densities to maximize profit, they can require antibiotics and other treatments for diseases, most of which end up in the water.[35]

Figure 2. Top Aquaculture-Producing Countries, 2006

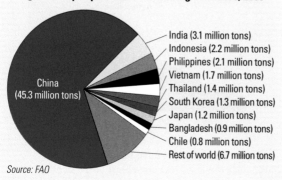

- India (3.1 million tons)
- Indonesia (2.2 million tons)
- Philippines (2.1 million tons)
- Vietnam (1.7 million tons)
- Thailand (1.4 million tons)
- South Korea (1.3 million tons)
- Japan (1.2 million tons)
- Bangladesh (0.9 million tons)
- Chile (0.8 million tons)
- Rest of world (6.7 million tons)

China (45.3 million tons)

Source: FAO

Figure 3. Farmed Shrimp and Salmon Production, 1950–2006

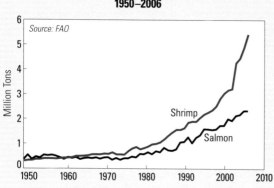

Source: FAO

These problems have led some researchers and fish farmers to consider alternative practices that would minimize environmental harm while allowing increased aquaculture production. For example, integrated fish farming works at the ecosystem level, using a combination of fish, shellfish, and aquatic plants to filter wastes and provide a self-sustaining source of food.[36] Integrated fish farming has been used outside major urban areas to raise fish for food and treat human wastes at the same time.[37]

With an ongoing food crisis and a growing world population, seafood production could potentially play a vital role in addressing food security and meeting development goals. Fish is highly nutritious and can be an important source of vitamins, minerals, and protein, even when consumed in minimal amounts.[38] A recent World Bank survey showed that small-scale fish farming consistently pays off for workers by raising income, creating stable work, and increasing food supplies.[39] However, not all seafood production is created equal: overfishing is linked to poverty, leading to fewer jobs and taking away an important source of income in developing countries.[40]

Energy and Transportation Trends

Vincent Kessler/Reuters

Solar cells on a barn roof, Weinbourg, France

For data and analysis on energy and transportation trends, go to www.worldwatch.org/vsonline.

Coal Use Rises Dramatically Despite Impacts on Climate and Health

James Russell

In 2006, coal accounted for 25 percent of world primary energy supply.[1] (See Figure 1.) Due to its high carbon content, coal was responsible for approximately 40 percent of the carbon dioxide (CO_2) emissions from fossil fuels, despite supplying only 32 percent of fossil fuel energy.[2] Management of this plentiful but heavily polluting energy resource has tremendous implications for human welfare, the health of ecosystems, and the stability of the global climate.

World coal consumption reached a record 3,090 million tons of oil equivalent (Mtoe) in 2006, an increase of 4.5 percent over 2005.[3] (See Figure 2.) China led world coal use with 39 percent of the total. The United States followed with 18 percent. The European Union and India accounted for 10 percent and 8 percent, respectively.[4] (See Figure 3.)

In terms of growth, China is even more dominant. The increase in China's coal consumption accounted for more than 70 percent of global growth in 2006 and more than 60 percent of the increase in world coal use over the past decade. India, responsible for just over 10 percent of the growth in the last 10 years, ranks a distant second.[5]

According to preliminary data, five new coal-fired generators with a combined capacity of 600 megawatts came online in the United States in 2006, while India added 930 megawatts of capacity.[6] In startling contrast, China brought online about as much coal power capacity each week as the United States and India together did over the entire year, adding an unprecedented 90 gigawatts in 2006.[7] Several studies have highlighted the uncertainty of China's energy statistics, however.[8] For example, some of the capacity reportedly added is likely to have been unauthorized projects completed earlier that were retroactively approved in 2006.[9] Nonetheless, the magnitude and trend of China's capacity additions and associated appetite for energy from coal are certain.

Worldwide, the extraction and combustion of coal have severe health and environmental impacts. In the United States, 47 workers were killed in coal mine accidents in 2006, while China's State Work Safety Supervision Administration reported a staggering 4,746 deaths.[10]

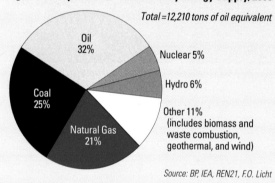

Figure 1. Composition of Total Primary Energy Supply, 2006

Total =12,210 tons of oil equivalent

Oil 32%
Nuclear 5%
Hydro 6%
Other 11% (includes biomass and waste combustion, geothermal, and wind)
Coal 25%
Natural Gas 21%

Source: BP, IEA, REN21, F.O. Licht

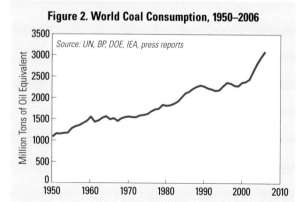

Figure 2. World Coal Consumption, 1950–2006

Source: UN, BP, DOE, IEA, press reports

Million Tons of Oil Equivalent

And the pollution emitted by coal-burning power plants and factories affects the health of millions of people. A recent World Bank study identified coal combustion as China's largest source of outdoor air pollution, to which it attributed 350,000–400,000 premature deaths a year.[11] Though these numbers were censored by Chinese authorities, at other times officials have acknowledged that coal power plants often do not comply with environmental regulations.[12]

Even in the United States, which is far ahead of China in terms of pollution control, the struggle to control hazardous emissions from coal power plants continues. In October, American Electric Power agreed to a record environmental enforcement settlement that requires the company to reduce annual sulfur dioxide and nitrogen oxide emissions by over 800,000 tons. The resulting improvement to air quality is expected to produce health benefits worth $32 billion per year.[13]

The longevity of coal-fired power plants and the abundance of coal suggest that decisions on new capacity made today will have enduring consequences. The average age of currently operating U.S. plants is 47 years, indicating that plants built today are likely to remain in operation for many decades.[14] Coal's abundance is apparent in reserve-to-production ratios, which based on current extraction rates exceed 200 years in the United States and India.[15] The figure in China is roughly 50–70 years, with an estimated total coal resource that allows room for plenty of reserve growth.[16]

Recent forecasts of world coal consumption in 2050 range from 2,900 Mtoe in a scenario published by the International Energy Agency (IEA), which assumes adoption of a stringent, worldwide carbon policy, to 10,700 Mtoe in a business-as-usual scenario published by the Massachusetts Institute of Technology (MIT).[17] Meeting any climate stabilization target will require control of coal emissions.[18] Nicholas Stern, who led an influential study on the economics of climate change, says that "unless we get coal under control, we're not going to be able to solve this problem."[19] After reaching this same conclusion, numerous studies identify carbon capture and sequestration (CCS) as a way to reconcile coal's importance as an energy resource with its role as a major contributor of CO_2 emissions.[20]

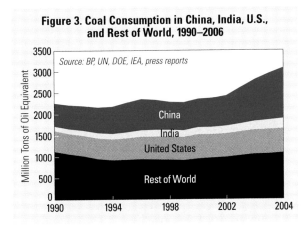

Figure 3. Coal Consumption in China, India, U.S., and Rest of World, 1990–2006

Source: BP, UN, DOE, IEA, press reports

Carbon capture and sequestration from a coal-fired power plant involves four key steps: isolate a relatively pure stream of CO_2 from the combustion source, pressurize the captured gas and transport to the storage site, inject the CO_2 into the storage reservoir, and monitor the storage reservoir for stability and leakage.[21] Each of these steps is already used in some commercial applications, mostly in oil and natural gas production and processing operations.

One project stands out for having successfully integrated all four steps, albeit not on a power plant. The Great Plains Synfuels plant in North Dakota produces synthetic natural gas from lignite coal. Since 2000, the facility also captures CO_2 from the "synthesis gas," an intermediate product, compresses that CO_2, and transports it 300 kilometers by pipeline to the Weyburn oil field. There the flow of CO_2, currently about 8,000 tons per day, is injected into the oil field to enhance oil production. A measurement study headed by the IEA concluded that the CO_2 injected at Weyburn will be sequestered there for thousands of years.[22]

The overall climate benefit of this particular

project is marred by the fact that the extra oil production it enables, an estimated 130 million barrels, will itself release over 50 million tons of carbon dioxide when burned.[23] Future CCS projects will need to inject CO_2 into deep saline aquifers rather than active oil fields in order to provide the scale of benefit required. The technology needed is not significantly different, but the project economics are currently much more challenging.

With the technical feasibility of CCS largely proved by Great Plains Synfuels and other demonstration projects, cost is the largest single factor preventing the deployment of this technology. Initial interest focused on applying CCS to advanced power plants known as an integrated gasification combined-cycle (IGCC) plants in anticipation of a lower overall project cost. An IGCC plant converts solid coal into a synthetic gas, from which CO_2 can be more easily extracted, and then uses that gas to produce electricity with relatively high efficiency. It is estimated that electricity produced by an IGCC power plant equipped with carbon capture will cost 35 percent more than electricity from a conventional plant. Adding CCS to a conventional power plant could increase the cost of electricity by upwards of 60 percent.[24] Transport, injection, and monitoring of the CO_2 will push these price premiums even higher. Thus without a sizable cost applied to carbon emissions, CCS is prohibitively expensive.

At present, cost estimates for coal-fired power plants equipped with CCS include a high degree of uncertainty, however. If and when the various CCS processes are commercialized, the technology that offers the lowest cost option will almost certainly vary from one project to the next, depending on many factors, including the quality of coal and whether the plant is new construction or a retrofit.[25]

Numerous research and development projects are working to reduce costs, and demonstration projects have been proposed in Europe, North America, Australia, and China.[26] The U.S. Department of Energy suggests that large-scale units may be completed around 2020, but an MIT study published this year finds current programs to commercialize carbon sequestration to be "completely inadequate," highlighting the need for further demonstration "at-scale" and advanced measurement, monitoring, and verification of storage.[27] Pilot operations scheduled to come online in 2007/08 may validate certain capture technologies, but the most aggressive proposals for at-scale applications of integrated CCS to coal-fired power plants target 2011/12.[28] In the meantime, each new coal plant will be a major source of additional CO_2 emissions.

Growing acknowledgement of the climate, health, and environmental consequences of coal use have led to mounting political opposition to new coal plants in the United States and Europe. A European Union commitment to reduce CO_2 emissions at least 20 percent by 2020 presents a formidable obstacle to any new coal power there that does not incorporate CCS.[29] Though a similar U.S. commitment has not been made, Senate majority leader Harry Reid recently took a stand against new coal power plants, and the state of California effectively banned state utilities from building new plants without CCS.[30] In mid-2007, the uncertain outlook for coal power resulting from burgeoning anti-coal activism was cited by Citigroup analysts in their decision to downgrade the stocks of all coal companies.[31]

On a global scale, the declining fortune of coal in industrial countries is overshadowed by its dominance in the energy mix of large developing economies. In China and India, coal maintains a preeminent role in plans to meet sustained, rapid growth of energy demand.[32] A true reconciliation of the coal resource and the climate risk that it presents must soon confront coal power on its new home turf.

Oil Consumption Continues Slow Growth

Joe Monfort

Global demand for oil reached 85.7 million barrels per day in 2007, a modest 1-percent increase over the 84.9 million barrels consumed daily in 2006.[1] (See Figure 1.) This marked the third straight year in which oil demand grew at an annual rate of less than 2 percent.[2] Despite the slow growth in demand, oil prices rose from just above $50 in January to near $100 at year's end—close to the all-time inflation-adjusted price record that was reached in the early 1980s.[3]

The United States continued unchallenged as the world's single largest oil-consuming nation in 2007, using almost one fourth of the global total at a rate of 20.7 million barrels daily.[4] But U.S. oil consumption was virtually unchanged for the third year in a row, as rising oil prices discouraged demand despite three years of steady economic growth.[5]

China increased its petroleum consumption by 5.5 percent in 2007, up from 7.3 million barrels per day in 2006 to 7.7 million barrels.[6] It now accounts for nearly 9 percent of the world's total oil use.[7] Over the past decade China has nearly doubled its oil consumption, and the share of global oil used by all nations that do not belong to the Organisation for Economic Co-operation and Development (OECD) has increased from 37 percent in 1997 to almost 43 percent in 2007.[8] Other top consumers in 2007 were OECD-Europe at 15.4 million barrels and Japan at 5 million barrels daily.[9] (See Figure 2.)

The crude oil spot price in the United States averaged $72 per barrel in 2007, a 9.5-percent increase over the 2006 average of $66 and nearly triple the average price in 2002.[10] The price of oil averaged over $90 a barrel in the final two months of 2007 and the first two months of 2008, nearing real dollar prices not seen since April 1980. On March 3rd, prices closed at $102.42, having set a new inflation-adjusted record high earlier during intra-day trading.[11] (See Figure 3.) The U.S. Energy Information Administration (EIA) projects an average of $87 a barrel for 2008 as a whole.[12]

These high prices in the face of slowing demand growth have contributed to increasing recognition that limited spare oil production capacity has fundamentally changed world oil

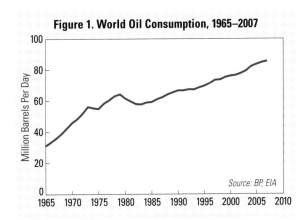

Figure 1. World Oil Consumption, 1965–2007

Source: BP, EIA

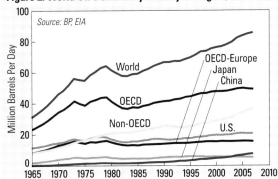

Figure 2. World Oil Demand by Country or Region, 1965–2007

Source: BP, EIA

markets over the last several years.[13] World crude oil production (without the natural gas liquids included in the consumption figures cited earlier) actually fell from 73.8 million barrels per day in 2005 to 73.2 million barrels a day in the first 10 months of 2007, according to EIA.[14] This makes 2005 the peak year for world oil production so far, though it is too early to know if this will turn out to be the all-time high.[15]

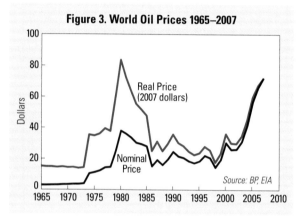

Figure 3. World Oil Prices 1965–2007

Source: BP, EIA

In 2007, crude oil production declined in some of the world's largest producers—including Indonesia, Mexico, Nigeria, Norway, the United Kingdom, and Venezuela—due to a combination of geological and political factors.[16] Saudi oil production continued to fall in 2007—a voluntary pullback to accommodate a softening market, according to Saudi officials.[17] By late 2007, however, Saudi production was 8 percent below the peak level reached in 2005, despite the fact that oil prices had risen roughly $20 per barrel since then.[18] Uncertainty over the condition of Saudi oil fields and their ability to increase or perhaps even sustain current production levels is the single largest unknown facing world oil markets.

Meanwhile, crude oil production rose in 2007 in Angola, Brazil, Canada (mainly from tar sands), China, and Russia, which surpassed Saudi Arabia to become the largest producer.[19] But production growth continues to slow in

Russia, an ominous sign since that nation has been the most important source of production gains over the past decade.[20]

The fact that the world is having a hard time expanding oil supply fast enough to keep up with even modest growth in demand is beginning to be accepted in some corners of the oil industry. The CEO of Royal Dutch Shell and the U.S. industry–dominated National Petroleum Council have both stated that supply constraints are likely to put continued pressure on world oil markets in the years ahead.[21] Although the dreaded phrase "peak oil" is still used mainly by oil industry mavericks like Matthew Simmons and T. Boone Pickens when discussing what lies ahead, their views—if not their language—do appear to be spreading to the mainstream.[22]

Political instability contributed to supply disruptions and price volatility throughout many of the world's oil-producing regions in 2007. Iraq reached its highest level of oil production since the U.S.-led invasion in 2003, but this still remains below prewar production levels.[23] In 2007, Iraq raised its production 5 percent over the 2006 figure, with gains in the latter half of the year coinciding with the 2007 "troop surge."[24] Overall, though, tensions in the Middle East remain highly charged and continue to factor heavily into world supply and price activity.

In Nigeria, despite a ceasefire signed by the government and eight rebel groups in December, the Movement for the Emancipation of the Niger Delta and other factions continue to wreak havoc on oil operations in the oil-rich southern delta.[25] As a result of pipeline sabotage, kidnappings of foreign workers, and other risks, Nigerian oil production has decreased 15 percent from its summer 2005 peak to an average production of 2.1 million barrels per day in 2007.[26] In Algeria, terrorist attacks targeting, among other sites, a United Nations office have also affected world markets and sparked concern among foreign oil companies operating in North Africa—a region considered crucial to future oil production.[27]

Thanks to skyrocketing oil prices, many oil companies again enjoyed record profits in 2007.

Chevron Corporation posted a company-best $18.7 billion in profit, while Royal Dutch Shell PLC reported a near-best $31.3 billion.[28] Exxon-Mobil Corporation, the world's largest publicly traded oil company, posted a 2007 net income of $40.6 billion, the single largest annual profit in U.S. corporate history.[29]

The long-term future of oil companies may not be so bright, however. ExxonMobil reported a decline in oil and natural gas production in 2007, and many companies are finding it hard to replace their reserves.[30] Not only have the largest oil fields already been developed, most of the promising prospect areas are controlled by state-owned oil companies, which hold 80 percent of the world's proven oil reserves.[31]

Wind Power Continues Rapid Rise

Janet L. Sawin

Global wind power capacity reached 94,100 megawatts by the end of 2007, up 27 percent from the previous year, and then topped 100,000 megawatts by April 2008.[1] (See Figure 1.) The roughly 20,000 megawatts installed in 2007 was 31 percent above the 2006 record for capacity additions.[2] (See Figure 2.) New wind installations were second only to natural gas in the United States as an additional source of power capacity and were the leading source of new capacity in the European Union (EU).[3]

The United States led the world in new installations for the third year in a row with a record-shattering 5,244 megawatts of wind capacity added, increasing cumulative installed capacity by 45 percent.[4] (See Figure 3.) Wind power represented 30 percent of new U.S. capacity additions last year, compared with 1 percent of the total just five years earlier.[5] The nation's wind capacity now totals 16,818 megawatts, second only to Germany, and is enough to power 4.5 million U.S. homes.[6] The surge in 2007 was driven by the federal production tax credit and by renewable energy mandates in 25 states and the District of Columbia.[7] The federal credit is due to expire at the end of 2008, though an extension is widely expected. Texas is the nation's top wind power generator, with 30 percent of total U.S. wind production last year, but six states now each have more than 1,000 megawatts of installed capacity.[8]

Wind capacity in the European Union rose 18 percent in 2007, with new records in several countries.[9] Wind power accounted for about 40 percent of new power installations across Europe.[10] Additions of 8,554 megawatts—an increase of 12 percent over 2006 installations— brought the EU's total to 56,535 megawatts.[11] Total wind capacity installed in Europe by the end of 2007 was enough to meet nearly 4 percent of the region's electricity demand in an average wind year and will avoid about 90 million tons of carbon dioxide emissions annually.[12] For the first time in several years, Europe's wind market dropped below half of the global total as the EU accounted for only 43 percent of new additions worldwide; but Europe still has 60 percent of total global capacity.[13]

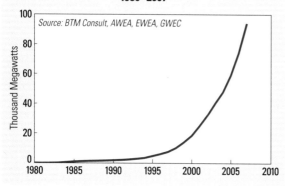

Figure 1. World Wind Energy Generating Capacity, 1980–2007

Source: BTM Consult, AWEA, EWEA, GWEC

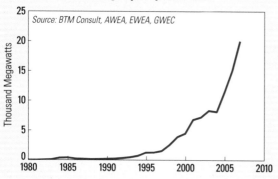

Figure 2. Annual Additions to World Wind Energy Generating Capacity, 1980–2007

Source: BTM Consult, AWEA, EWEA, GWEC

Germany remains the world leader in wind power capacity, with a total of 22,247 megawatts, almost 24 percent of the global total.[14] However, Germany's wind market experienced a significant slowdown in 2007. Rising turbine prices in conjunction with falling payments to wind-generated electricity have temporarily made the German market less attractive to developers than the U.S. and British markets are; Germany has also experienced an increasing scarcity of good onshore sites.[15] Only 1,667 megawatts of new capacity were installed in 2007, 25 percent less than added during the previous year.[16] Despite this, the share of electricity that Germany obtained from renewable sources—half of which comes from wind power—continues its rapid rise.[17] Wind power generated the equivalent of 7.2 percent of Germany's electricity consumption in 2007.[18] Windy northern Schleswig-Holstein now aims for the wind to generate all of that state's power by 2020, up from 30 percent today.[19]

Spain led Europe in new installations in 2007, now ranking third worldwide in total wind capacity. An estimated 3,522 megawatts were added last year, bringing the nation's total to 15,145 megawatts, enough to meet 10 percent of Spain's electricity needs.[20]

Other countries in Europe that experienced significant growth in 2007 include France (888 megawatts added), Italy (603), Portugal (434), and the United Kingdom (427), and each of these countries now has total capacity of well over 2,000 megawatts.[21] The United Kingdom and Portugal, however, both experienced slower growth than in 2006.[22]

Although Europe (mostly Germany and Spain) and the United States now account for 78 percent of the world's installed wind power capacity, more than 70 nations—from Australia to Zimbabwe—now tap the wind to produce electricity.[23]

The biggest surprise is China, which was barely in the wind business three years ago but which in 2007 trailed only the United States and Spain in wind installations and was fifth in total installed capacity.[24] An estimated 3,449 megawatts of wind turbines were added in 2007, bringing China's provisional total to 6,050

megawatts and already exceeding the government's target for 2010.[25] (An estimated one fourth of this capacity is still not connected to the grid, however, due to planning problems.)[26] Another 4,000 megawatts are expected to be added in 2008 and, based on current growth rates, the Chinese Renewable Energy Industry Association predicts that China's wind capacity could reach 50,000 megawatts by 2015.[27]

Figure 3. Annual Wind Capacity Additions in China, Germany, Spain, and the United States, 1980–2007

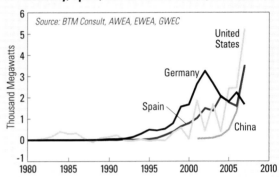

Elsewhere in Asia, India added 1,730 megawatts of new capacity and continues to rank fourth overall for total installations, with an estimated 8,000 megawatts.[28] Other regions and countries experiencing significant growth include Canada (added 386 megawatts), New Zealand (151), Latin America, where Brazil added 161 megawatts and Chile installed about 18 megawatts, and northern Africa, where Egypt added 80 megawatts.[29]

These dramatic increases in capacity took place against a backdrop of serious turbine shortages. Wind turbines require some 8,000 components, and suppliers of many of these parts need years to ramp up production.[30] Parts shortages have affected the United States in particular, where numerous projects have been put on hold.[31] As a result, several European companies that had the funds and foresight to lock in orders of new machines have taken this opportunity to buy up smaller companies and utilities to gain a foothold in the United States, where wide open spaces promise an enormous future market.[32]

Manufacturers are now positioning themselves to increase production of gearboxes, rotors, and other components, and it is expected that this will eliminate the turbine shortage by sometime in 2009.[33] For the short term, however, the turbine shortage could dictate how quickly the industry will grow.[34]

These growing pains have affected the economics of wind power. Over the past 15 years, the costs of wind-generated electricity have dropped by 50 percent, while efficiency, reliability, and power rating have all experienced significant improvements.[35] But costs have increased in recent years due to the turbine shortage, rising material costs, and increased manufacturing profitability.[36] (In the United States, costs have also risen thanks to the falling value of the dollar relative to the euro.) Despite the higher costs, wind power remains competitive with new natural gas plants, and all conventional plants have seen similar construction cost increases.[37] Wind power will become increasingly competitive with coal as more countries put a price on carbon.

The global wind market was estimated to be worth about $36 billion in 2007, accounting for nearly half of all investments in new renewable power and heating capacity last year.[38] As many as 200,000 people around the world are currently employed by the wind industry.[39] These numbers will only rise in coming years.

The EU is now committed to generating 20 percent of its primary energy with renewables by 2020, which means that these sources will need to provide about 35 percent of the region's electricity in 12 years, up from 15 percent in 2007.[40] Wind power is expected to account for most of that increase.[41] And the potential for the United States, China, and many other countries is enormous.

The wind industry has consistently blown by past projections—BTM Consult ApS, for example, forecast in 2002 that global capacity would reach 83,000 megawatts by the end of 2007, far short of the 94,100 megawatts that it actually did achieve—and it could continue to do so for years to come.[42]

Despite Obstacles,
Biofuels Continue Surge

Joe Monfort

World production of biofuels rose some 20 percent to an estimated 54 billion liters in 2007.[1] (See Figure 1.) These gains meant biofuels accounted for 1.5 percent of the global supply of liquid fuels, up just 0.25 percent from the previous year.[2]

Global production of fuel ethanol—derived primarily from sugar or starch crops—increased 18 percent to 46 billion liters in 2007, marking the sixth consecutive year of double-digit growth.[3] Production of biodiesel—made from feedstock such as soy, rape and mustard seed, and palm and waste vegetable oils—rose an estimated 33 percent, to 8 billion liters.[4]

The United States, which produces ethanol primarily from corn, and Brazil, which primarily uses sugarcane, account for 95 percent of the world's ethanol production.[5] (See Figure 2.) Brazil increased its ethanol production by 21 percent in 2007, to 19 billion liters.[6] But the United States continued to widen its lead over Brazil as the world's leading producer by boosting output 33 percent to 24.5 billion liters in 2007.[7]

The United States now accounts for a little more than half of the world's ethanol production, and though the industry has encountered some roadblocks, strong growth is still expected, with an estimated 15 billion liters from 68 new or expanding bio-refineries in 2008.[8] Despite this boom, the United States still imported an estimated 1.7 billion liters of ethanol last year, 40 percent of which came from Brazil.[9] Most gasoline sold in the country in 2007 was blended with ethanol.[10]

Germany maintained its lead in biodiesel by increasing production capacity 60 percent in 2007.[11] The German biodiesel market has weakened, however, since the government started taxing biodiesel sales in late 2006 and imposed a second round of taxes at the beginning of 2008.[12]

These taxes, coupled with soaring feedstock prices, have eliminated biodiesel's price advantage.[13] Several large producers have announced production cuts, and overall output is now falling well short of available capacity.[14] Other European countries posting biodiesel production capacity gains include Austria, Belgium, Greece, Italy, the Netherlands, Poland, and Portugal.[15]

Figure 1. Ethanol and Biodiesel Production, 1975–2007

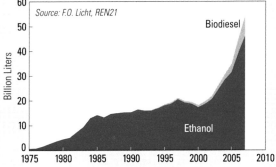

Figure 2. Fuel Ethanol Production in World, Brazil, and United States, 1975–2007

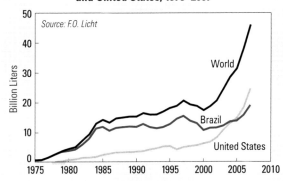

Biodiesel production continued to grow rapidly in Southeast Asia, where Malaysia seeks to capture 10 percent of the global biodiesel market by 2010 through expansion of its palm oil plantations. Indonesia aims to expand its palm oil plantations to 1.5 million hectares by 2008.[16]

The primary forces underpinning the continued surge in biofuel production and capacity expansion were a combination of blending mandates and tax subsidies in several countries, with strong support from agricultural interests.[17]

The U.S. Energy Independence and Security Act of 2007 expanded the U.S. Renewable Fuels Standard, calling for the use of 136 billion liters of biofuels in 2022 (with 60 billion liters of that total mandated for cellulosic ethanol).[18] Other renewable fuels policies enacted in 2007 include the United Kingdom's adoption of a 5-percent target by 2010, Japan's goal to produce 6 billion liters per year by 2030, and China's annual production targets of 13 billion liters of ethanol and 2.3 billion liters of biodiesel by 2020.[19] The European Union (EU) is considering expanding its biofuels target of 5.75 percent by 2010 to a higher percentage, as part of an obligation to use renewables for 20 percent of the region's energy consumption by 2020.[20] In total, at least 17 countries have enacted mandates for blending biofuels into vehicle fuels, with an additional 36 states and provinces in 21 countries taking similar actions in recent years.[21]

In response to these market signals and policy incentives, worldwide investment in biofuel production capacity continued to expand in 2007.[22] The value of biofuel production plants announced or under construction exceeds $4 billion in the United States, $4 billion in Brazil, and $2 billion in France.[23] However, overall investments in biofuels decreased from the record set in 2006 as feedstock prices soared and socio-environmental concerns mounted.[24]

In the public markets, biofuel companies raised $1 billion in equity, approximately $2 billion less than in 2006.[25] Rising commodity prices, deforestation and carbon sink concerns, and uncertain energy content levels all affected investor confidence in biofuel stocks in 2007,

and shares in the sector lost 19 percent of their value during the year.[26] Venture capital and private equity investments in biofuel firms also decreased slightly from 2006.[27]

Last year the U.N. Food and Agriculture Organization (FAO) reported that biofuel demand has played a key role in driving 8 percent of food price inflation in China, 13 percent in Indonesia and Pakistan, and 10 percent or more in Latin America, Russia, and India.[28] Adding to these concerns, FAO reported that wheat has doubled in price, that global food reserves are at their lowest level in 25 years, and that costly food aid to developing countries has declined.[29] While climbing biofuel production and demand represents just one influential factor in this trend, the International Monetary Fund and other multilateral agencies report that using food to produce biofuels will continue to strain already scarce water and arable land resources.[30]

Soaring biofuels production has also produced a substantial backlash as grain and soybean prices have soared and the environmental benefits of biofuels have been called into question. Recent studies conclude that clearing grass and forestlands to produce ethanol and other biofuels could potentially double the output of greenhouse gas emissions instead of reducing them, as previously thought.[31]

Palm oil, once considered a promising new eco-friendly fuel source, now faces similar questions and is blamed for contributing to massive deforestation and the subsequent loss of enormous tropical carbon sinks.[32] With the recent Bali round of international climate negotiations dealing explicitly with deforestation, which accounts for 20–25 percent of all carbon dioxide emissions, it is unclear how the biofuel industries in countries such as the United States, Indonesia, and Brazil will react.[33]

One outcome of these developments has been a growing number of governmental and nongovernmental initiatives aimed at addressing concerns associated with biofuel production. EU countries recently reached an initial agreement on sustainability standards for biofuels that would require biofuel energy sources to emit 35 percent less greenhouse gases than the equivalent fossil fuels before 2015 and 50 percent less after 2015.[34]

California Governor Arnold Schwarzenegger also announced in January 2007 that his state would establish a Low-Carbon Fuel Standard and would begin developing metrics for measuring the "life-cycle carbon intensity" of all transportation fuels.[35] This metric will eventually be incorporated into California's implementation plan for alternative fuel use. Industry-led non-governmental organizations such as the Roundtable on Sustainable Palm Oil have also started investigating sustainable supply chain standards and consumer labels to help distinguish feedstock products in the market.[36]

Mounting problems with conventional biofuels spurred investment in advanced biofuel feedstocks and technologies in 2007—including cellulosic ethanol that can be produced from waste materials and non-food crops that can be grown on marginal land.[37]

Another Sunny Year
for Solar Power

Janet L. Sawin

Global production of photovoltaic (PV) or solar cells—which convert the sun's light directly to electricity—increased 51 percent in 2007, to 3,733 megawatts.[1] (See Figure 1.) According to early estimates, more than 2,935 megawatts of solar modules were installed that year, bringing cumulative global installations of PVs since 1996 to more than 9,740 megawatts—enough to meet the annual electricity demand of more than 3 million homes in Europe.[2] (See Figure 2.) Over the past five years, annual global production of PV cells has increased nearly sevenfold, and cumulative installations have grown more than fivefold.[3]

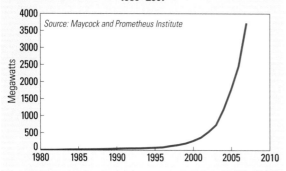

Figure 1. Annual Global Production of Photovoltaic Cells, 1980–2007

Source: Maycock and Prometheus Institute

Europe—led by Germany—passed Japan to lead the world in PV manufacture, producing an estimated 1,063 megawatts of solar cells in 2007, up 56 percent over 2006.[4] (See Figure 3.) About 40,000 people are now employed in the PV industry in Germany alone, and the German company Q-Cells outproduced Japan's Sharp to become the number one manufacturer worldwide.[5]

Germany remains the world's top PV installer, accounting for almost half of the global market in 2007.[6] Thanks to the country's feed-in tariff for renewable electricity, which requires utilities to pay customers a guaranteed rate for any renewable power they feed into the grid, Germans installed about 1,300 megawatts of new PV capacity, up from 850 megawatts in 2006, for a total exceeding 3,830 megawatts.[7] As capacity has risen, PV installed system costs have been cut in half in Germany between 1997 and 2007.[8] PVs now meet about 1 percent of Germany's electricity demand, a share that some analysts expect could reach 25 percent by 2050.[9]

Japan continued to produce more PV cells than any other individual country, with 920 megawatts manufactured in 2007.[10] But Japan's share of the world total fell from 37 percent in 2006 to just below 25 percent.[11] Unable to compete with China and Taiwan for low-cost solar cells, Japanese manufacturers have changed tactics and are looking beyond conventional crystalline silicon cells to thin-film technology.[12] Domestic installations in Japan declined from 286 megawatts in 2006 to an estimated 230 megawatts in 2007.[13]

China climbed rapidly to become the second largest cell-producing nation after Japan, manufacturing about 820 megawatts of PVs and accounting for 22 percent of global production.[14] But annual production capacity reached almost 1,590 megawatts by the end of the year, well ahead of any other country (though still 9 percent below all of Europe).[15] Despite these impressive numbers, the Chinese market for PVs remains small, and much of the 20 megawatts of new capacity installed in 2007 was for remote off-grid applications.[16] Taiwan is also experiencing dramatic growth in production, manufacturing 368 megawatts of cells in 2007 and ending the year with the capacity to produce 710 megawatts annually.[17]

Spain ranked second after Germany for total installations in 2007 but accounts for only an estimated 3 percent of global production.[18] According to estimates, Spain added anywhere from 425 to 640 megawatts in 2007, up from fewer than 100 megawatts in 2006.[19] This puts the country well ahead of the government's official target of 400 megawatts by 2010.[20] The market in Spain is being driven by a strong guaranteed price for PV electricity.[21]

In the United States, cell production rose 48 percent to 266 megawatts.[22] Although this represents a dramatic increase in production from the once world-leading U.S. solar industry, the nation's shares of global production and installations continued to fall in 2007. PV cell production accounted for only 7 percent of the global total, down slightly relative to 2006.[23] But U.S. manufacturers are now focused on the "next wave" of solar technologies: in 2007, the United States accounted for approximately two thirds of global thin-film production.[24]

An estimated 150 megawatts of new grid-connected PV capacity was installed in the United States in 2007, up about 45 percent over the previous year, putting the nation in fourth place for total capacity—behind Germany, Japan, and Spain. [25] California continued to dominate the U.S. market, though growth was slower than expected because of changes in state incentive levels and a weak dollar.[26] U.S. utilities are beginning to recognize the potential value of solar PV: in early 2008, Southern California Edison announced plans to install 250 megawatts of distributed capacity over the next five years.[27]

Other countries becoming major players include Italy (25–50 megawatts installed), South Korea (50 megawatts), and France (45 megawatts), all thanks to new or strengthened feed-in laws.[28] In addition, India installed an estimated 20 megawatts, and Portugal added 10 megawatts.[29] Some of Portugal's additions were part of a large solar plant that came online in early 2007 and will generate enough electricity to meet the needs of 8,000 households.[30]

Such strong growth occurred against a back-

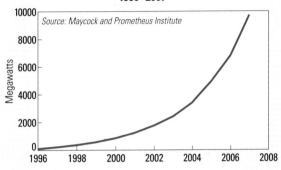

Figure 2. Cumulative Global Sales of Photovoltaic Modules, 1996–2007

Source: Maycock and Prometheus Institute

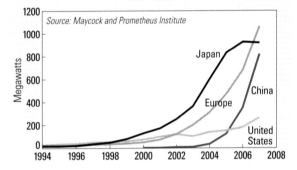

Figure 3. Photovoltaic Production, by Country or Region, 1994–2007

Source: Maycock and Prometheus Institute

drop of polysilicon shortages—supply has been tight since 2005, driven mainly by strong policies pushing demand growth.[31] However, significant new capacity will start to come online in the second half of 2008.[32] The European Photovoltaic Industry Association projects 80,000 tons of annual production by 2010, up from just over 37,000 tons in 2007.[33] Some analysts are predicting excess capacity within the next few years, and in early 2008 China-based Trina Solar canceled plans for a new 10,000-ton polysilicon production facility.[34]

The current shortage is driving advances in thin film technologies, which require no polysilicon. Thin films are composed of very thin layers of photosensitive materials and require less energy and materials to make than conventional silicon-based solar cells and are cheaper to produce.[35] They can be integrated into roof shingles, siding, and the windows of buildings.[36] After decades of market disappointment, thin-film production has increased nearly fourfold in the past two years, claiming more than 10 percent of the global market in 2007.[37]

Performance data for such technologies are relatively limited, and efficiencies remain low compared with conventional solar cells.[38] But the situation is rapidly improving—commercial efficiencies rose from 9 to 10 percent in 2007, and in early 2008 researchers at the U.S. National Renewable Energy Laboratory set a new record at 19.9 percent efficient, close to commercial levels for conventional cells.[39] Because of the potential for dramatic cost reduction, many researchers view thin films as the future of solar.[40] The solar industry attracted $3 billion in equity during 2007, with some of the biggest investments going to young solar companies in the United States and to thin-film technologies.[41]

Scientists are also working on a range of third- and fourth-generation PV technologies.[42] German researchers have developed a prototype solar module that uses organic dyes combined with nanoparticles, applied to glass with a screen printing technique, to generate electricity.[43]

Konarka Technologies successfully conducted its first demonstration of manufacturing PV cells with ink-jet printing in early 2008.[44] And companies in the United States and Europe are exploring ways to turn road surfaces into solar power generators.[45]

Thanks to economies of scale, rising conversion efficiencies, and more-efficient use of polysilicon in conventional cells, average PV module prices declined in 2007, even as polysilicon prices rose.[46] Stronger than expected demand growth in Spain helped keep global PV prices higher in 2007 than some had predicted.[47] But analysts and industry leaders alike expect continued price reductions in the near future through further economies of scale and increased optimization in assembly and installation.[48] The Prometheus Institute projects that installed system prices for large projects will fall 50 percent by 2010, to $4 per watt peak (without incentives) in the best locations.[49]

Solar electricity is likely to become cost-competitive with the retail price of electricity in many parts of the world in the next several years. As Jesse Pichel of New York's Piper Jaffray said recently: "Whether it's 2010, 2012, or 2015, I think everyone can see the writing on the wall."[50] When solar becomes competitive with conventional power, "solar power demand is infinite."[51]

Vehicle Production Rises,
But Few Cars Are "Green"

Michael Renner

According to Global Insight, global passenger car production in 2007 rose to 52.1 million units from 49.1 million the previous year.[1] In addition, production of "light trucks" ran to 18.9 million, up from 17.9 million in 2006, for a combined total of 74.1 million.[2] Global Insight projects 2008 total production to reach 75.8 million.[3] (See Figure 1.) Including unused production capacity, the world's auto companies are capable of churning out some 84 million vehicles per year. PricewaterhouseCoopers projects that by 2015 worldwide capacity to grow to 97 million units.[4]

Japan produced the most vehicles in 2007, 11 million, closely followed by the United States with 10.5 million.[5] China's production continues to surge, reaching 8.1 million vehicles in 2007. Projected 2008 output of 9.3 million would bring it almost to a par with the United States, whose production is expected to decline to 9.5 million units. [6] The next largest producers are Germany (6 million) and South Korea (4 million).[7] (See Figure 2.) France, Spain, Brazil, Canada, and Mexico each produced between 2 million and 3 million units.[8] At 1.95 million vehicles, India is close to joining the top 10.[9]

The world's fleet of passenger vehicles is now an estimated 622 million, up from 500 million in 2000 and a mere 53 million in 1950.[10] China continues to expand not only its production but also its domestic car ownership. There are now an estimated 43–47 million vehicles on the road there—about as many as the United States had in 1947.[11] India's love affair with the automobile is taking off too. And when the country's Tata Motors unveiled the "Nano" in 2008—a no-frills vehicle advertised as the world's cheapest car—it made a splash around the world.[12]

The transport sector, which relies heavily on cars and trucks for freight movement, is responsible for about a quarter of the world's energy use and has the fastest-rising carbon emissions of any economic sector.[13] Road transport currently accounts for 74 percent of the world's total transport-related carbon dioxide (CO_2) emissions.[14]

Improved fuel economy not only limits energy consumption but translates directly into

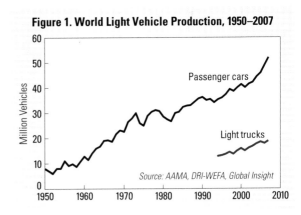

Figure 1. World Light Vehicle Production, 1950–2007

Source: AAMA, DRI-WEFA, Global Insight

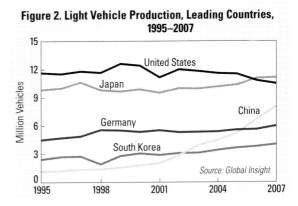

Figure 2. Light Vehicle Production, Leading Countries, 1995–2007

Source: Global Insight

reduced emissions of carbon dioxide. It can also help reduce air pollution from vehicles, although fuel economy and lower emissions of sulfur and nitrogen oxides or particulate matter do not necessarily go hand in hand.[15] Lowering air pollution depends on both improvements in engine technology and the production of cleaner fuels (especially those with lower sulfur content). Japan and the United States, followed by the European Union, have the most stringent emission limits.[16] China and India are introducing regulations that follow those of the European Union, though with a time lag of several years.[17]

Hybrid vehicles are generally seen as a key means to achieve higher fuel efficiency, although this technology can be equally applied to boost acceleration and horsepower. In 2007, a total of 541,000 hybrids were produced.[18] PricewaterhouseCoopers projects that by 2015 some 2.2 million of these vehicles might be produced.[19]

Toyota, the company that popularized such cars with the introduction of the Prius in 1997, in 2007 reached the milestone of a cumulative 1 million hybrids produced.[20] The company sold half of these vehicles in the United States, where it commands a cumulative 73-percent share of the hybrid market.[21] All in all, 2.2 percent of U.S. light-duty vehicle sales were hybrids in the 2007 model year.[22] By 2015, hybrids might reach a U.S. market share of anywhere between 5 and 11 percent.[23] In Japan, car companies sold close to 89,000 hybrid passenger vehicles in 2006, for 1.6 percent of all cars sold.[24]

European countries have embraced diesel-powered cars (which account for 50 percent of total sales there), since diesels consume 30 percent less fuel than gasoline engines and emit 25 percent less CO_2.[25] Worldwide, demand for diesel-powered light vehicles is projected to increase from 16 million in 2007 to 29 million in 2017, resulting in an increase in market share from a current 23.6 percent to 31.5 percent.[26] Evolving engine technology and cleaner fuels have rendered diesel passenger cars substantially cleaner than in the past, especially with regard to sulfur dioxide emissions. However, they still emit far more nitrogen oxides and par-

ticulate matter than cars that use gasoline do.[27]

A 2007 report by the International Council on Clean Transportation concludes that Japanese and European factories produce the most-efficient vehicles available today, with new passenger vehicles scoring roughly 40 miles per gallon (mpg) on average.[28] The United States is at the bottom of this international ranking, while countries like China, Canada, and Australia are in between and working to increase efficiency in coming years.[29]

In 1998, European, Japanese, and South Korean companies selling vehicles in Europe entered into a voluntary agreement with the European Commission to lower the amount of carbon emitted by new passenger cars.[30] The goal was to reduce the 1995 level of 186 grams of CO_2 per kilometer to 140 grams by 2008/2009.[31] According to Commission reports, just over 26 percent of European-produced vehicles met the goal in 2004.[32] For Japanese- and Korean-made cars sold in the European Union, the numbers were 21 and 29 percent, respectively.[33] Because cars have become heavier and more muscular, the industry is not expected to achieve its voluntary aim. In response, the European Commission adopted a proposal forcing manufacturers to produce cars that emit 130 grams per kilometer by 2012 and said it would present further measures in pursuit of a goal of 120 grams.[34]

The United States has scorned higher fuel efficiency for more than two decades.[35] Following the first oil crisis of the early 1970s, sales of the biggest gas-guzzlers—those achieving 15 mpg or less—declined dramatically, from 67 percent of sales in model year 1975 to just 4.5 percent in 1982.[36] (See Figure 3.) But the bulk of vehicle sales remains in the interval between 15 and 25 mpg, and the recent popularity of SUVs has even led to reversals of fuel economy gains.[37] Just 1.2 percent of all U.S. light vehicles in the 2007 model year could be categorized as truly fuel-efficient—that is, achieving at least 35 miles per gallon, and thus roughly on a par with European carbon limits.[38] On average, new U.S. cars in 2007 emitted about

180 grams of carbon per kilometer.[39]

Leadership in pursuing fuel economy and reducing carbon emissions is essential if the industry is to avoid a head-on collision with climate stability. The motor vehicle industry is a cornerstone of modern economies and an important source of jobs. But a relatively small share of the industry's current output—and thus its employment base—can be considered sustainable. Using the 120 grams of CO_2 per kilometer limit as a threshold, about a quarter-million of the automobile manufacturing industry's global workforce of 8.4 million jobs can be considered a shade of green: 150,000 out of more than 2 million jobs in Europe, 62,000 out of 820,000 in Japan, 10,000 out of 250,000 in South Korea, and 13,000 out of 1.1 million in the United States.[40]

Thailand's government is encouraging efficient vehicle production in an innovative way.[41] The government decided in June 2007 to grant tax incentives to auto manufacturers that produce small, fuel-efficient "eco-cars."[42] In order to receive tax breaks, a company must, among other things, produce cars that get at least 20 kilometers per liter (47 mpg), generate no more than 120 grams of CO_2 per kilometer, and meet Euro-4 air emissions standards.[43] The country's 182,000-strong auto industry workforce produced just under 300,000 cars and 896,000

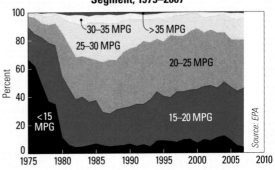

Figure 3. U.S. Light Vehicle Sales, by Fuel Economy Segment, 1975–2007

Source: EPA

commercial vehicles (mostly small pickup trucks) in 2005.[44] Thailand has the potential to become a regional hub of "eco-car" production, with plans to serve markets in other Asian countries, Australia, and Africa.[45]

Due to a lack of data, calculations on "green" jobs are not possible at the moment for other major vehicle-producing countries, such as China (with 1.6 million employees), Russia (755,000), Brazil (289,000), and India (270,000).[46] But China and India are targeting small car production, with China's Chery compact model reportedly achieving a fuel rate of 27 kilometers per liter, equivalent to 63 mpg.[47]

Nuclear Power Crawling Forward

Jim Riccio

In 2007, global installed capacity of nuclear power grew by less than 2,000 megawatts to 372,000 megawatts.[1] (See Figure 1.) The slight growth in nuclear power is attributable to the addition of three new reactors in India, China, and Romania.[2] The new nuclear capacity is equivalent to just one tenth of the new wind power installed globally in 2007.[3]

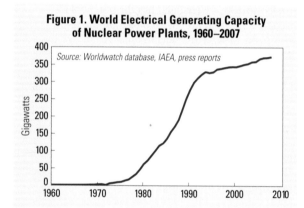

Figure 1. World Electrical Generating Capacity of Nuclear Power Plants, 1960–2007

Source: Worldwatch database, IAEA, press reports

Rising gas prices and concern about the carbon dioxide emissions from coal plants have fueled growing interest in nuclear power in many nations.[4] But only four countries began building new nuclear reactors in 2007: China, France, Russia, and South Korea.[5] The seven new reactors being built in those countries will account for 5,190 megawatts of new nuclear capacity—about 100 megawatts less than was added in 2006.[6] (See Figure 2.)

No nuclear reactors were permanently shut down in 2007.[7] Since 1964, however, the commercial nuclear industry has retired 124 reactors, amounting to a total of 36,800 megawatts of generating capacity.[8] (See Figure 3.)

By the end of 2007, some 34 reactors were under construction worldwide, but 12 of these units have been under construction for 20 years or more.[9] In the Americas, only two reactors are being built, in the United States and Argentina; both began construction in the 1980s.[10] In Western Europe two reactors are being built, in Finland and France.[11] In Eastern Europe, reactors are under construction in Bulgaria and Ukraine (two each), Slovakia (two), and Romania (one).[12]

In Russia, seven reactors—totaling 4,585 megawatts of electric capacity—are being built; four of these have been in construction for two decades.[13] Russia is completing a fast-breeder reactor, which produces more nuclear fuel that it consumes and which uses plutonium, highly enriched uranium, or even mixed oxide fuel rather than the conventional fuel, uranium.[14] In addition, construction has begun on two 30-megawatt reactors that will be placed on barges to provide power to remote regions.[15]

The U.K. government has indicated interest in resuming its long-dormant nuclear construction programs, but it will have to navigate long, uncertain regulatory processes before any new plants can be started.[16]

Asia accounts for the most nuclear power plant construction, with 20 new reactors currently under way.[17] India and China each have six reactors under construction.[18] These 12 plants account for 8,130 megawatts—or more than a quarter of the nuclear capacity currently being built worldwide.[19] South Korea is building three units, while Japan, Iran, and Pakistan are each building a single nuclear plant.[20]

Some nuclear projects are being delayed by construction problems. The expected delivery date of the Olkiluoto Finnish plant has been pushed back by at least two years because of concerns about concrete in the foundation and flawed welds for the reactor's steel liner, among other problems.[21] Analysts estimate the problems at this reactor could add another 1.5 billion euros to the final price tag, increasing by 50 percent the initial projected cost of 3 billion euros.[22]

Engineering challenges are also slowing the Chinese and Taiwanese nuclear programs. China's newest reactor was two years behind schedule when it went into commercial operation in 2007. Construction was delayed for almost a year as Chinese regulators examined the welds of the steel liner of the reactor core.[23] Despite these setbacks, the government continues to forge ahead with nuclear power. French nuclear giant Areva and the Chinese government will cooperate on future nuclear reactors as well as the reprocessing of nuclear waste.[24]

In Taiwan, the Lungman reactors have fallen five years behind schedule, due in part to welds that failed inspection in 2002 and had to be redone.[25] In addition, the Taiwan Power Company acknowledged that "the rising cost of steel, concrete and other commodities has gutted subcontractor profits, causing them to stop work to renegotiate fixed price contracts."[26]

In Japan, nuclear power suffered a setback in July 2007 when a major earthquake struck the Kashiwazaki-Kariwa nuclear plant on the northwest coast, the largest nuclear complex in the world.[27] The earthquake, measuring 6.8 on the Richter scale, required operators to shut down the plant's seven nuclear reactors, which account for 8,000 megawatts of Japan's nuclear capacity.[28] Officially, the complex is slated to remain inactive for at least one year. However, because the quake caused ground motion two and a half times more powerful than the reactors were designed to withstand, questions have been raised about whether they should ever be returned to service.[29]

In the Middle East and Africa, there is only one nuclear reactor currently under construction: a Russian-designed 1,000-megawatt reactor in Iran.[30] But the Iranian nuclear program has spurred interest in the region. In the past year, more than a dozen Middle Eastern countries

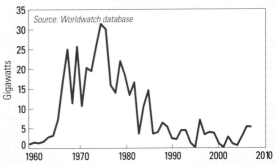

Figure 2. World Nuclear Reactor Construction Starts, 1960–2007

Source: Worldwatch database

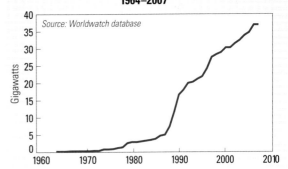

Figure 3. Nuclear Capacity of Decommissioned Plants, 1964–2007

Source: Worldwatch database

have announced they intend to pursue the development of nuclear power.[31] The interest expressed by majority Sunni Muslim states is viewed by U.S. officials as a direct response to the nuclear ambitions of Shiite Iran.[32]

In the United States, no new nuclear construction was initiated in 2007, though one reactor was restarted after a 22-year shutdown, and construction resumed on a reactor that had been stalled since 1988.[33] Nuclear corporations submitted applications for seven new reactors in 2007, the first ones proposed in at least 30 years, and government regulators expect applications for another 22 reactors in 2008.[34] Yet even nuclear industry officials have questioned whether new reactors are economically viable without government subsidies. The president of Constellation Generation Group, an energy company that is planning to build a reactor in the state of Maryland, has stated that it will not build nuclear plants without loan guarantees.[35]

Wall Street has yet to be sold on new nuclear investments in the United States. Moody's, a credit rating agency, has stated that it "believes that many of the current expectations regarding new nuclear generation are overly ambitious," raising questions about the industry's cost estimates and its schedule for bringing the next U.S. nuclear reactor online.[36] Moody's noted that the costs associated with next-generation nuclear plants could be significantly higher than the estimates of approximately $3,500 per kilo-

watt cited by the industry.[37] Moody's noted that its estimates were $6,000 per kilowatt, and it cautioned that nuclear investment could affect corporations' credit ratings.[38]

Moody's concerns seem well placed. By the end of 2007, new nuclear plant cost estimates for identical Westinghouse-designed nuclear plants had soared, more than doubling to $12–18 billion.[39] MidAmerican Energy Holdings, a subsidiary of Warren Buffett's Berkshire Hathaway Inc., became the first U.S. company to postpone plans for a new reactor when it withdrew its letter of intent to government regulators in late 2007.[40] MidAmerican's spokesperson stated that it does not currently make economic sense to pursue this project.[41]

Strong Growth in Compact Fluorescent Bulbs Reduces Electricity Demand

Alice McKeown and Nathan Swire

Between 2001 and 2006, production of compact fluorescent lamps (CFLs) in China—which accounts for roughly 85 percent of global output—tripled from 750 million to 2.4 billion units.[1] (See Figure 1.) The total number of CFLs in use globally nearly doubled between 2001 and 2003 alone, growing from an estimated 1.8 billion to 3.5 billion units.[2]

Reliable global data on CFL use since 2003 do not exist, but sales growth in individual countries strongly indicates that total usage continues to increase at a fast pace. Between 2000 and 2004, for example, estimated sales in the United States grew 343 percent—from 21 million to 93 million—and by 2007 they reached 397 million.[3] CFL sales in Western Europe grew 34 percent between 2000 and 2004, from 173 million to 232 million units, and in Eastern Europe they rose 143 percent, from 23 million to 56 million units.[4] (See Figure 2 and Table 1.)

The lightbulb market share for CFLs varies widely among leading industrial nations. In the United States, CFLs accounted for more than 20 percent of sales in 2007, a strong growth from less than 1 percent before 2001.[5] But other wealthy nations have shown much higher CFL use rates for quite some time, including 80 percent of households in Japan and 50 percent in Germany (in 1996 in both cases).[6] Many developing countries have shown strong CFL market share in recent years as well: 14 percent of sales in China in 2003, for instance, and 17 percent in Brazil in 2002.[7]

CFLs are far more efficient than traditional incandescent lightbulbs because they produce less heat to create light, using about 75 percent less energy to produce the same amount of light and lasting up to 10 times longer.[8] These energy savings translate into monetary savings. For example, a single CFL bulb can save up to

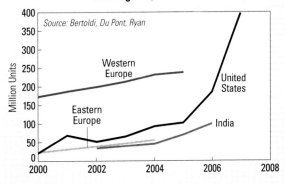

Figure 1. CFL Production in China, 2001–06

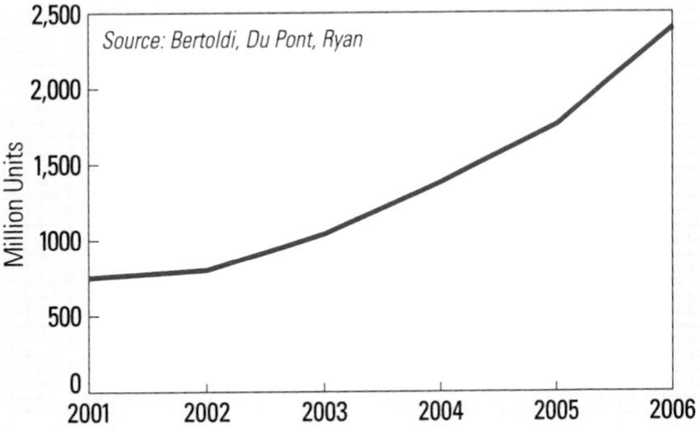

Source: Bertoldi, Du Pont, Ryan

Figure 2. CFL Sales in Selected Countries and Regions, 2000–07

Source: Bertoldi, Du Pont, Ryan

$30 in energy costs in the United States over its lifetime; savings can be even greater where electricity costs are higher.[9] Incandescent bulbs burn out after around 1,000 hours of use while CFLs can last for up to 10,000 hours, lowering their cost even without taking energy savings into account.[10]

Energy savings also mean a reduction in

Table 1. Estimated World Sales of Compact Fluorescent Lamps, 1988–2006

Year	Sales
	(million units)
1988	45
1989	59
1990	83
1991	112
1992	138
1993	179
1994	206
1995	245
1996	288
1997	362
1998	387
1999	452
2000	528
2001	750*
2002	800*
2003	1,040*
2004	1,380*
2005	1,760*
2006	2,400*

*Includes China's production only, which accounts for roughly 85 percent of world production. Global sales data not available after 2000.

Source: Scholand; Du Pont.

greenhouse gases. Electric lighting consumes 19 percent of total electricity grid production and is responsible for more than 1,500 million tons of carbon dioxide (CO_2) per year, the equivalent of the emissions from more than half of the world's light passenger vehicles.[11] Replacing all the inefficient incandescent lightbulbs with CFLs in the United States alone could prevent 158 million tons of CO_2 emissions according to one lighting company, the equivalent of taking more than 30 million cars off the road.[12] Substituting CFLs under a global scenario that minimizes costs would reduce lighting energy demand by nearly 40 percent and save 900 million tons of CO_2 a year by 2030, with a cumulative savings by then totaling 16.6 billion tons—more than twice the carbon dioxide released in the United States in 2006.[13]

A large part of the increase in CFL sales has been due to government action. In 2007, Australia became the first country to ban the sale of incandescent bulbs, and sales there will be phased out entirely by 2009.[14] The European Union, Ireland, and Canada have since announced plans to ban incandescent bulbs.[15] The United States has also passed legislation increasing the efficiency standard required for lightbulbs, which will effectively phase out incandescents.[16] In total, more than 40 countries have announced plans to follow suit.[17]

Retail giant Wal-Mart has also promoted the use of CFLs by raising awareness, and the company's action is driving down prices. In November 2006 Wal-Mart announced a goal of selling 100 million CFL units by the end of 2007—which it accomplished by October that year.[18]

Despite their many benefits, CFLs have some problems, including quality control at factories in developing countries. To address this issue, the Efficient Lighting Initiative (ELI), launched in 1999 by the International Finance Corporation and the Global Environment Facility, created a certification mechanism for high-quality products.[19] ELI allows manufacturers to voluntarily have their products tested to see if they meet a technical standard for quality. Those that pass receive ELI's "seal of approval," a well-known international standard, and can qualify for promotions and procurement programs.[20]

Modern CFLs also contain about 4 milligrams of mercury, a dangerous neurotoxin.[21] This is less than 1 percent as much mercury as found in old thermometers, but it still means broken bulbs should be treated with care and discarded bulbs should be recycled instead of thrown out.[22] And for consumers who rely on coal-fired electricity, one of the largest sources of mercury emissions, the increased energy efficiency of these bulbs means that over its lifetime a CFL—even if it is broken or thrown away—will release significantly less mercury into the environment than an incandescent bulb would.[23]

Because of these issues with CFLs, many scientists and consumers have looked toward light-emitting diodes (LEDs) as a better source of energy-efficient lighting. LEDs are semiconductor pinpoint lights that when clustered together can function as a lightbulb. They are more than twice as efficient as CFLs and can last five times as long.[24] However, LEDs also have several drawbacks, such as high cost (up to $60 per bulb), a harsh white light that consumers find unappealing, and a more focused light stream that is not well suited for ambient lighting.[25] These problems have prevented LEDs from catching on with consumers. But as they are improved through new research and development, LEDs could become the next generation of energy-efficient lighting.[26] Recent market projections indicate that LEDs could become cost-competitive with CFLs in as little as five years.[27]

One Twelfth of Global Electricity Comes from Combined Heat and Power Systems

Amanda Chiu

Just over 8 percent of world electricity generating capacity uses cogeneration, also known as combined heat and power (CHP)—an integrated energy system that produces both electricity and heat.[1] Cogeneration plants have a total global installed electricity capacity of some 325,000 megawatts (MW).[2]

Combined heat and power captures waste heat as electricity is produced and recycles it to provide another energy service, unlike conventional systems in which heat is simply exhausted into the environment and additional fuel must be used to provide the same amount of heat to industry or buildings. Another form of cogeneration captures waste energy from industrial processes and recycles it into useful electricity and thermal power.

The advantage of combined heat and power over separate generation is efficiency. An average coal-fueled power plant converts 33 percent of its fuel to usable energy services.[3] The most efficient, natural gas–fueled plant has a conversion efficiency of 60–64 percent.[4] In contrast, CHP systems have efficiency ratings of 75–90 percent, with lower losses from transmission and distribution of electricity due to the close proximity of the generator and consumer and with fewer condensation losses in boilers.[5]

CHP uses waste heat to produce electricity or useful heat for industrial processes, district heating and cooling systems, and residential and commercial buildings.[6] District heating and cooling either heats buildings through steam in well-insulated pipe networks or cools them by funneling the steam through absorption chillers that distribute cool water.[7] In addition to these large-scale applications, cogeneration can be used to supply electricity and heat to individual or dense groups of residential and commercial buildings. In North America, this application is most often found in universities and hospitals.[8]

Because a good deal of thermal heat is lost when it is transported, CHP plants must be located near the point of use to be most effective. The ideal site is near consumers who need power and heat for more than 5,000 hours throughout the year.[9] Industrial plants have been ideal locations for these facilities, as they demand a constant supply of electricity and heat, which minimizes the ramping up and down of CHP systems. District heating and cooling systems using cogeneration are most valuable in regions with cold climates, like Finland, or high population densities.[10]

Although combined heat and power was used before 1900, it fell out of favor in the twentieth century as power production became more centralized and as coal power plants were linked to poor air quality. As electricity generators were forced to move away from population centers, CHP became uneconomical.[11] But after the oil shocks of the 1970s, its efficiency advantages persuaded many countries to take another look at this technology.

Most CHP systems are found in energy-intensive sectors, including paper and printing, chemicals, metal and oil refining, and food processing, which together account for 80 percent of world installed capacity.[12] Because CHP relies on diverse technologies that use a variety of fuels, including renewables, it can be a climate-friendly way of producing power. Recent data indicate that natural gas accounts for 53 percent of world CHP capacity, with coal at 36 percent, and oil at 5 percent.[13] Renewable fuels like biomass and high-temperature geothermal supply 6 percent but, along with municipal solid waste and landfill gas, are starting to get more attention.[14]

The regions that rely the most on cogeneration are Western and Eastern Europe. More than half of Western Europe's CHP-generated electricity is produced in publicly owned facilities connected to district heating and cooling systems.[15] Denmark is the global leader, with CHP meeting 52 percent of its electricity needs (5,690 MW) in 2003 (see Figure 1), over six times the world share, and with most of that capacity tied into district heating systems.[16]

Almost 13 percent of Germany's electricity (21,203 MW) was generated from CHP in 2005, and the government projects that figure could eventually reach 57 percent.[17] The vast majority of CHP there is found in industry. Germany is well positioned to become the world leader in both biogas CHP and micro-CHP for smaller-scale commercial and residential installations.[18]

In Eastern Europe, CHP accounts for almost 19 percent of total power production, with an installed CHP capacity of approximately 35,000 MW (based on national data for 2001 through 2004), the result of Soviet-era centralized planning, which called for widespread use of cogeneration technology.[19] The systems need to be modernized, however, and European governments and CHP companies are becoming interested in such projects in Russia.[20]

CHP in the United States accounts for a relatively modest 8 percent of power production, although the nation is the world leader in total installed capacity, with 84,707 MW operating in 2003.[21] (See Figure 2.) As in Germany, most of U.S. CHP capacity is in industry. More than 85 percent of U.S. capacity is large-scale—over 50 MW—and almost 65 percent is over 100 MW.[22] The United States has the potential to produce between 110,000 and 150,000 MW of electricity with CHP systems.[23]

In China, almost 13 percent of the nation's electricity (28,153 MW) and 60 percent of urban central heating is generated with CHP.[24] Still, China is estimated to have tapped into less than 20 percent of its industrial potential, and the National Development and Reform Commission has set a goal of 200,000 MW of CHP by 2020—which would be 22 percent of the installed power capacity expected that year.[25]

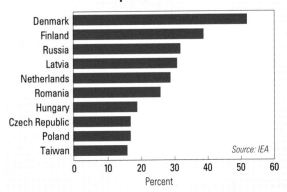

Figure 1. CHP Share of National Power Production, Top 10 Countries

Source: IEA

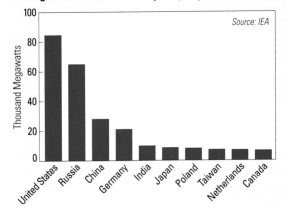

Figure 2. Installed CHP Capacity, Top 10 Countries

Source: IEA

Although countries with little or no demand for district heating or cooling are not expected to shift to cogeneration for that purpose, industrial CHP still has great potential in these nations. Brazil is a hydropower-based economy with little demand for another form of power generation. Yet CHP fueled by biomass is entering the industrial sector, particularly the sugar sector, and could produce 17 percent of Brazil's electricity by 2030.[26]

A few countries, like Finland, need little government incentive to implement CHP; elsewhere a wide variety of policy measures are used to stimulate CHP growth.[27] Denmark and Germany give distributed generators access to the electricity grid through standardized technology and give CHP and renewable generators higher priority when grid operators are deciding which power plant to run. Germany requires utilities to purchase CHP-generated electricity at the higher cost of average alternative generators rather than the actual generation cost (feed-in tariffs).[28] Denmark removed its purchase obligations in 2005 but still has a feed-in tariff in place and is promoting biomass fuels through a pricing premium.[29] The Danish government incorporates heating provision into city planning and gives investment subsidies for CHP retrofitting, while German authorities exempt buildings with CHP-based district heating and cooling from renewable energy requirements in building codes.[30]

Climate-related legislation, such as a carbon tax in Finland and Denmark and allocation of emissions rights in the Netherlands and Germany, promotes CHP and acknowledges its efficiency advantages.[31] The United States promotes CHP technology through eight CHP Regional Application Centers and the Combined Heat and Power Partnership.[32]

Due to its higher efficiency, CHP can help countries not only reduce fuel demand but also meet greenhouse gas emissions reduction targets. The United States could expand its CHP capacity to displace 11 quadrillion BTUs of fuel a year—about 11 percent of total U.S. energy consumption.[33] In addition, fewer new power plants would be needed. And renewable fuels could be used in cogeneration plants instead of fossil fuels, yielding further climate benefits. Biomass gas, landfill gas, wood waste, and anaerobic digester gas show the most promise in the United States.[34]

According to the International Energy Agency, CHP could reduce global greenhouse emissions by at least 4 percent in 2015 and 10 percent in 2030.[35] This translates into a 7-percent overall cost reduction in the power sector, or $795 billion.[36]

CHP expansion faces similar regulatory barriers worldwide: obstructive regulations and laws, financial incentives favoring established technologies, and a lack of awareness about the technology.[37] Recent developments, however, signal heightened interest in CHP. A 2004 European Union directive charged its member states to look at their potentials for CHP and address barriers to its wider use.[38] And in 2007 the G8 industrial nations made a commitment to take action to increase energy efficiency and CHP use in electricity generation.[39] With momentum building toward the 2009 post-Kyoto climate negotiations, combined heat and power is becoming an energy efficiency tool of choice to tackle the climate change crisis.

Bicycle Production Reaches
30 Million Units

Gary Gardner

Bicycle production was up 3.2 percent in 2007 to 130 million units, a continuation of the upward trend that has characterized production for most of this decade.[1] (See Figure 1.) Global output continued to be largely a Chinese affair, as China produced two of every three bikes made worldwide.[2] (See Figure 2.) India, the European Union, Taiwan, Indonesia, and Brazil were the next five largest producers, accounting together for about a quarter of the total.[3]

Cycling is potentially an important mode of sustainable transport: it is non-polluting, inexpensive, and good for users' health and the quality of urban life. But the amount of cycling in most cities worldwide remains well below its potential.

The share of all trips made by bike varies greatly among countries. Chinese cities still register some of the highest cycling rates in the world, despite growing consumer interest in private automobiles. In the most cycled cities, such as Tianjin, Xi'an, and Shijiazhuang, the bicycle accounts for more than half of all trips.[4] In the west, the Netherlands, Denmark, and Germany have the highest rates of cycling, ranging from 10 to 27 percent of all trips.[5] This compares with about 1 percent of trips in the United Kingdom, the United States, and Australia.[6]

In Africa, where bicycles are often unaffordable and where walking is generally the dominant transportation mode, cycling's share of trips registers in the single digits except in a few medium-size cities such as Morogoro, Tanzania; Eldoret, Kenya; and Ougadougou, Burkina Faso, where 10–23 percent of trips are made by bike.[7]

Electric bikes, which use an electric motor to assist pedaling, are a burgeoning market segment, with most production again taking place in China.[8] Sales of electric bikes in Germany nearly tripled in 2007.[9] For aging populations and for riders tackling hilly terrain or facing hot tempera-

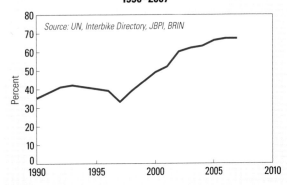

Figure 1. World Bicycle Production, 1950–2007

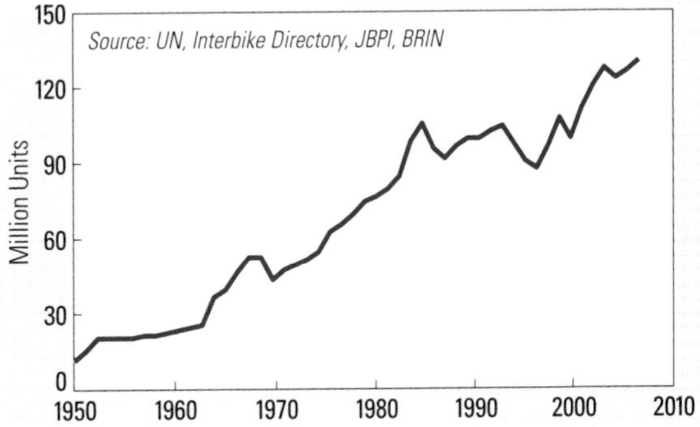

Source: UN, Interbike Directory, JBPI, BRIN

Figure 2. Chinese Share of World Bicycle Production, 1990–2007

Source: UN, Interbike Directory, JBPI, BRIN

tures, electric bikes make cycling a viable transport option. Yet battery disposal poses a potentially significant environmental downside to e-bikes.

Increases in global commodity prices in 2007 and 2008 could soon affect bicycle production. Price hikes for steel, butyl, rubber, titanium, and other materials are driving up production costs, and materials shortages have left tens of thousands of partially completed bikes in warehouses.[10]

At the same time, the spike in gas prices in the first half of 2008 began to stimulate cycling, especially among commuters.[11] Dealers began to stock bikes and accessories in anticipation of increased demand.[12] In some U.S. cities, including Toledo in Ohio and Charlotte in North Carolina, rising gas prices led officials to resurrect or start police bicycle patrols.[13] The Trek Bicycle Corporation reports increased sales of police bikes for the past three years.[14]

The Netherlands, Denmark, Germany, and other European nations reached high cycling rates through policies that give priority to cycling, walking, and public transportation over private automobiles.[15] Bikeways that are separated from traffic, stoplights timed to the speed of bikes, shortcuts allowing cyclists to make right-hand turns before intersections, traffic calming in residential neighborhoods, ample bicycle parking, and coordination with public transport have all made cycling safe, fast, and convenient in strong biking cities.[16] (See the Video Resources section for links to videos that illustrate various biking infrastructure features.)

Placing importance on cycling in transportation and land use policy leads to an increase in cycling safety. Bicycle injuries per kilometer traveled are about 30 times higher in the United States than in the Netherlands, and cycling deaths are eight times higher there.[17] The sense of safety in the Netherlands has helped increase ridership even among the elderly: 24 percent of all trips made by elderly Dutch people are bike trips.[18]

Some cities are also increasing accessibility to cycling by establishing public bicycle rental programs.[19] Similar to car-sharing programs, these schemes make bikes available to subscribers at strategic locations citywide. Patrons pay on the order of $50 per year to subscribe, as well as a per-hour charge, although in many programs the first half-hour is free.[20] Users get access to a bike with an electronic card, use the bike as needed, and return it to the same or another parking rack when finished. In many cities, the program is paid for through on-bike advertising or through concessions to communications companies, who fund the programs in exchange for the right to erect new billboards and sell advertising on them.[21]

Copenhagen, Berlin, and other European cities have featured public bike programs like this for many years, and Paris took the concept to a new level in 2007–08 by making 20,600 bikes available at more than 1,450 rental stations—four times as many stations as subway stops—some of which are located about 300 yards apart.[22] Bikes are now essentially an extension of the public transportation system in Paris. Barcelona and Lyon have also started major programs in the last two years, and new initiatives are planned for Rome, London, Moscow, Geneva, Beijing, Tel Aviv, and Sydney, as well as in a few U.S. cities, including Washington, DC, and San Francisco.[23]

VIDEO RESOURCES

Several recent videos illustrate some advanced cycling infrastructure and programs from around the world.

- Biking to school in the Netherlands: http://tinyurl.com/cwwfbr
- A cycle roundabout in the Netherlands: http://tinyurl.com/dm8ctd
- Stoplights and bollards timed to favor bicycles in Odense, Denmark: http://tinyurl.com/dxfsw9
- A "bicycle lift" for steep hills in Trondheim, Norway: http://tinyurl.com/7re5du
- Secure, protected bicycle parking in France: http://tinyurl.com/cad9ab
- Highly automated bicycle parking in Japan: http://tinyurl.com/3u5vyb
- Simple, high-volume bike parking in Germany: http://tinyurl.com/c3cmfy
- The public bike system in Paris: http://tinyurl.com/5b39g6
- Rutgers University professor John Pucher's lecture on making cycling attractive: http://tinyurl.com/488cv5.

Environment and Climate Trends

Courtesy Greenpeace/Australia

Bleached coral on the Great Barrier Reef, Australia

For data and analysis on environment and climate trends, go to www.worldwatch.org/vsonline.

Climate Change Accelerates

James Russell

The year 2007 tied with 1998 as the second warmest year on record, with an average global temperature of 14.57 degrees Celsius (see Figure 1), according to NASA's Goddard Institute for Space Studies.[1] The average global temperature in 2007 was nearly 0.6 degrees Celsius greater than the average between 1951 and 1980 and more than 0.8 degrees Celsius above the average recorded from 1881 to 1910.[2] The World Meteorological Association ranks 1998–2007 as the warmest decade on record.[3]

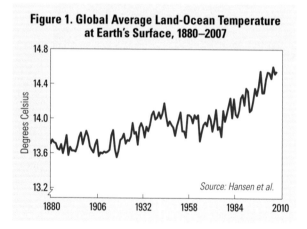

Figure 1. Global Average Land-Ocean Temperature at Earth's Surface, 1880–2007

Degrees Celsius

Source: Hansen et al.

That 2007 was so warm is particularly significant because throughout the year important cooling influences prevailed. These included low solar irradiance (the energy Earth receives from the Sun) and a strong La Niña in the Pacific. These natural processes were counteracted by the build-up of greenhouse gases caused principally by the combustion of fossil fuels, with other important contributions from agriculture, land use change, and industrial gases.[4] (See Figure 2.) In 2007, the concentration of atmospheric carbon dioxide (CO_2) climbed to a new

high of 383.6 parts per million.[5] (See Figure 3.)

The Intergovernmental Panel on Climate Change (IPCC) released its Fourth Assessment Report in 2007, in which it concluded with greater than 90 percent certainty that emissions of CO_2 and other greenhouse gases from human activities are driving climate change.[6] The report, which represents the work of thousands of experts and scientists, describes a litany of impacts to natural and managed systems that are already happening or are likely to occur if we continue with business as usual.[7]

Even if emissions stopped rising today, additional warming is inevitable due to the large inertia in the climate system. CO_2 persists in the atmosphere for 50–200 years, which means that current emissions will exert a warming influence for decades to come.[8] Meanwhile, the ocean, which acts as a vast heat sink, will continue to warm. As it does, air temperatures will likely rise to double the warming already witnessed.[9]

Current trends suggest that we may experience even more than this amount of warming. As anthropogenic emissions are rising, the efficiency of natural carbon sinks is in decline. A 2007 study led by the Global Carbon Project concluded with high confidence that the share of emissions absorbed by ocean and terrestrial sinks is falling; this, in turn, is accelerating the rise in atmospheric CO_2 concentration beyond the rate of emissions increase.[10]

While climate change is a global challenge, many global indicators—like average temperature—overlook the dramatic changes occurring at regional and local levels. The World Meteorological Organization reports that parts of Europe experienced winter and spring temperatures more than 4 degrees Celsius above average in 2007, and extreme drought struck North America and China.[11] Massive floods caused devastation in England, South Asia, and many South American countries.[12] While causal links cannot be made between climate change and specific weather events, more extreme weather is consistent with expectations for a warmer globe.

Warming in the northern hemisphere is more pronounced than the global average. Much of the Arctic experienced an average 2007 temperature that was greater than 2 degrees Celsius above the 1951–80 mean.[13] Arctic sea ice coverage reached a record low by September 1 (summer's end)—39 percent below the September 1 average over the 1979–2000 period and 23 percent below the coverage just two years earlier, in 2005—prompting scientists to predict a complete disappearance of summer sea ice by 2030.[14] Loss of sea ice creates a positive feedback in the climate system, as open water absorbs far more solar energy than ice and snow do, driving further warming.

Land-based ice melt is also increasing, with serious implications for coastal communities, wildlife, and ecosystems. Two major glaciers in southeast Greenland have lost approximately 122 cubic kilometers of ice each year since 2001, and scientists estimate that Greenland's contribution to sea level rise is now about 0.6 millimeters annually.[15] A recent study of Antarctica concluded that the continent is also experiencing a net ice loss and that the pace of ice melt accelerated 75 percent over the past decade.[16] According to the IPCC, land-based ice melt and thermal expansion caused sea levels to rise 3 millimeters per year between 1993 and 2003.[17]

The rapid pace of global environmental change is likely to exceed the capacities of many species to adapt. Coral reefs—vital in natural, cultural, and economic terms—appear particularly vulnerable to even the most modest climate change scenarios, as they are unable to adapt to rapid changes in temperature and ocean acidity.[18] A 2007 report to the U.S. Congress concluded that while some species could thrive in response to projected climate change, impacts on many others "may include extinctions, changes in species' ranges, mismatches in

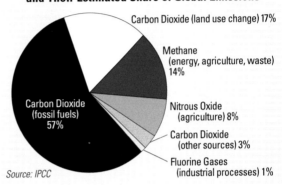

Figure 2. Important Greenhouse Gases, Major Sources, and Their Estimated Share of Global Emissions

Carbon Dioxide (land use change) 17%
Methane (energy, agriculture, waste) 14%
Carbon Dioxide (fossil fuels) 57%
Nitrous Oxide (agriculture) 8%
Carbon Dioxide (other sources) 3%
Fluorine Gases (industrial processes) 1%

Source: IPCC

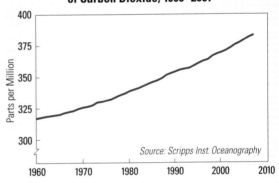

Figure 3. Atmospheric Concentration of Carbon Dioxide, 1960–2007

Source: Scripps Inst. Oceanography

their phenologies (timing of pollination, flowering, etc.), and population declines."[19] Further, "climate change acts in concert with other variables to effect changes in species," according to several studies cited in the report, and it is uncertain how wildlife will adapt.[20]

All this new information brought a sense of heightened urgency to the global discourse on climate change in 2007. In April, for the first time, the U.N. Security Council took up the issue of climate change and its potential impacts on peace and security.[21] Climate change was also addressed at the June meeting of the G8 in Germany, at a high-level U.N. summit in New

York in September, and at a U.S.-hosted gathering of the world's major economies, also in September.[22] The year concluded with the 192 parties to the U.N. Framework Convention on Climate Change agreeing in Bali to negotiate by 2009 a new global climate pact that will include plans for mitigation, adaptation, technology transfer, and financing.[23]

Carbon Emissions on the Rise
But Policies Growing Too

James Russell

In 2007, carbon emissions from fossil fuel combustion worldwide reached an estimated 8.2 billion tons, which was 2.8 percent more than in 2006—and 22 percent above the total in 2000.[1] The United States and Europe accounted for roughly 4 and 3 percent, respectively, of the growth during this decade.[2] India contributed 8 percent, and China, a staggering 57 percent.[3] Despite the rapid increase, China's 18.3 share of global fossil fuel emissions remained slightly behind the U.S. share (19.5 percent).[4] Per capita emissions in the developing world remain well below those in industrial countries.[5] (See Figure 1 and Table 1.)

Coal, oil, and natural gas are burned to produce electricity, to power engines, and to feed industrial processes. When burned, the carbon contained in these fuels is converted to carbon dioxide (CO_2), which is a natural component of Earth's atmosphere. CO_2 traps heat that would otherwise radiate into outer space, thereby keeping Earth's temperature within a habitable range.[6] But emissions from human activities have greatly increased the stock of carbon dioxide in the atmosphere. The additional gas is trapping more heat, raising the average global temperature and changing the climate.[7] Fossil fuels account for about 74 percent of all CO_2 emissions and for roughly 57 percent of all greenhouse gas emissions.[8] (See Figure 2.)

The combustion of coal typically releases 1.8 times as much carbon dioxide per unit of energy as natural gas does and 1.3 times as much as oil.[9] But since more oil than coal is used, total emissions from these two fossil fuels are similar.[10]

Carbon-to-energy ratios vary dramatically, depending on the methods used to produce the fuels. Liquid fuels derived from coal have nearly twice the global warming impact as equivalent fuels derived from petroleum.[11] Similarly, pro-

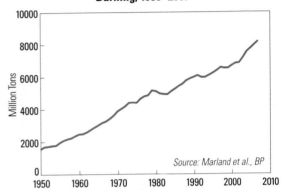

Figure 1. World Carbon Emissions from Fossil Fuel Burning, 1950–2007

Source: Marland et al., BP

Table 1. Total Fossil Fuel Carbon Emissions in 2007 and Emissions Relative to Population and Economy

Country or Region	Carbon Emissions from Fossil Fuels*	Carbon Emissions Per Person	Carbon Emissions Per GDP
	(thousand tons)	(tons)	(kilograms per thousand dollars GDP [PPP])
United States	1,630,000	5.4	120
China	1,530,000	1.2	220
Western Europe	910,000	2.1	66
India	420,000	0.4	140
Russia	420,000	3.0	200
Japan	360,000	2.8	84
Africa	310,000	0.3	160
World	8,220,000	1.2	130

Does not include emissions due to gas flaring.
Source: Based on Marland et al., BP, EIA.

Figure 2. Top Greenhouse Gases and Their Contributions to Global Emissions, by Source*

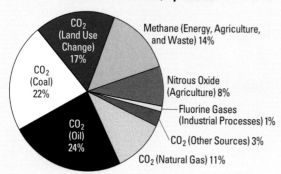

CO₂ (Land Use Change) 17%

CO₂ (Coal) 22%

CO₂ (Oil) 24%

Methane (Energy, Agriculture, and Waste) 14%

Nitrous Oxide (Agriculture) 8%

Fluorine Gases (Industrial Processes) 1%

CO₂ (Other Sources) 3%

CO₂ (Natural Gas) 11%

*Fossil fuel shares of CO₂ emissions based on 2007 data; all others based on 2004 data.

Source: Based on IPCC, Marland et al., BP, EIA

ducing oil from Canada's tar sands emits up to three times as much carbon as producing conventional oil, due to the energy-intensive extraction and refinement.[12] As conventional fossil fuels become scarcer, use of these carbon-intensive fuels is growing. Production of oil from Canada's tar sands reached 1 million barrels a day in 2004 and may reach 3–4 million barrels a day by 2015.[13]

Consumption of fossil fuels by the world's wealthiest countries is largely responsible for elevating atmospheric CO_2 levels to the current 384 parts per million, an increase of 37 percent over the pre-industrial level.[14] But today the rapid, coal-dependent development of China and India is the most important driver of growth in global carbon dioxide emissions. Coal provides 70 percent of commercial energy in China and 56 percent in India.[15] Recent trends suggest that most of the growth in emissions from human activities will come from the developing world. In fact, based on the average growth rates for the past five years (see Figure 3), China's emissions from fossil fuels will surpass those of the United States sometime in 2008.[16] Thus the key to stabilizing the global climate will be moving industrial nations to a low-carbon energy economy while ensuring that developing countries

can leapfrog to cleaner development paths.

The potential for de-carbonizing modern economies is huge. Energy efficiency, wind, solar, and hydro power are carbon-free energy alternatives that are available today.[17] Germany, for example, already gets 14 percent of its electricity from renewable sources and hopes to increase this to 45 percent by 2030.[18] A 2007 study by McKinsey & Company suggested that by 2030 the United States could affordably reduce greenhouse gas emissions to 28 percent below 2005 levels using a mix of measures, including energy efficiency, renewable energy, and carbon capture and storage.[19]

Action at the diplomatic and national policy levels to limit carbon emissions continues to advance. In December 2007, the 192 parties to the United Nations Framework Convention on Climate Change agreed to establish a new global climate change agreement by 2009.[20] This will build on the existing Kyoto Protocol, which commits industrial countries to reduce greenhouse gas emissions to 6–8 percent below their 1990 levels.[21] Under the existing agreement, emission targets have not been adopted by developing countries or the United States, and the initial commitment period is set to expire in 2012.[22] These issues need to be addressed before the conclusion of the negotiations in 2009.

To meet its commitments in the most cost-effective manner, the European Union (EU) established a carbon market known as the Emissions Trading Scheme (ETS). By establishing a carbon cap and associated carbon price, the ETS has succeeded in reducing emissions by some 5 percent.[23] The cap has been lowered to nearly 6 percent below 2005 levels for the 2008–12 period.[24] And last year the EU committed to reducing greenhouse gas emissions to 20 percent below 1990 levels by 2020.[25] If pursued by the most cost-effective policy approaches (including the ETS), these goals could be achieved at an estimated cost of about 0.6 percent of gross regional product in 2020.[26]

The U.S. Congress has struggled to formulate a similar nationwide climate change policy, and the country will not see climate change legislation before 2009, under a new administration.[27] Despite the delay at the national level, 19 states now have greenhouse gas emission reduction targets.[28] California plans to cut its emissions to 1990 levels by 2020 through sharp increases in energy efficiency and by using renewable sources to supply 33 percent of the state's electricity by 2030.[29]

In spite of relatively low emissions per person, the developing world has also begun to act to mitigate climate change. China's current Five-Year Plan includes a target of reducing the energy intensity of gross domestic product 20 percent below the 2005 level by 2010.[30] China has also adopted a plan to satisfy 10 percent of energy demand through renewables by 2010 and then 15 percent by 2020.[31] Costa Rica has joined Iceland, Norway, and New Zealand in a pledge to achieve zero net carbon emissions.[32] Although Costa Rica's emissions are only a tiny fraction of the global total, its commitment to carbon neutrality may serve as a wake-up call to wealthier countries.

According to a 2007 U.N. report, getting emissions back to today's levels by 2030 would require a global investment of about $200 billion annually, or 0.3–0.5 percent of the gross world product (GWP).[33] But achieving the reductions that scientists estimate are needed to

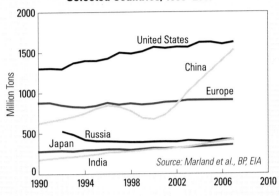

Figure 3. Carbon Emissions from Fossil Fuel Burning, Selected Countries, 1990–2007

Source: Marland et al., BP, EIA

limit global warming to 2 degrees Celsius will require bringing global emissions at least 50 percent below 2000 levels by 2050.[34] Economist Nicholas Stern has recently suggested that the dangers of climate change warrant an even greater investment—2 percent of GWP.[35] Though this is a massive sum, Stern's 2007 report, *The Economics of Climate Change*, concludes that the price of doing nothing to stop runaway carbon emissions could be as much as 5–20 percent of GWP.[36]

Weather-related Disasters Dominate

Petra Löw

In 2007, there were 874 weather-related disasters worldwide, a 13-percent increase over 2006 and the highest number since the systematic recording of natural perils began in 1974.[1] Weather-related disasters around the world have been on the rise for decades (see Figure 1): on average, 300 events were recorded every year in the 1980s, 480 events in the 1990s, and 620 events in the last 10 years.[2]

Figure 1. Weather-Related Disasters, Five-Year Averages, 1983–2007

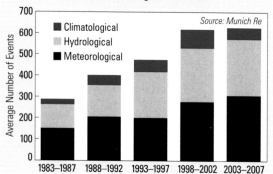

Weather-related disasters can be divided into meteorological, hydrological, and climatological events.[3] The category of meteorological events includes tropical cyclones (hurricanes, typhoons, cyclones), extratropical cyclones (winter storms), and local storms (severe storms, thunderstorms, hailstorms, snowstorms, and tornadoes). Hydrological events include floods (general floods, flash floods, storm surges/coastal floods) and wet mass movements (rockfalls, landslides, avalanches, subsidence). And climatological events include extreme temperatures (heat waves, cold waves, extreme winter conditions), droughts, and wildfires (forest fires, bush/brush

fires, scrub/grassland fires, urban fires).[4]

In 2007, weather-related disasters accounted for 91 percent of all natural disasters, a broader classification that also includes earthquakes, tsunamis, volcanic eruptions, and dry mass movements.[5] About 81 percent of economic losses from natural catastrophes and 97 percent of insured losses resulted from weather-related disasters.[6] And all six "great natural disasters" in 2007—three storms and three floods—were weather-related.[7] A "great natural disaster" occurs if the affected region's ability to help itself is overstretched and supraregional or international assistance is required. As a rule, this is the case when there are thousands of fatalities, when hundreds of thousands of people are made homeless, or when the overall losses or the insured losses reach exceptional orders of magnitude.

Economic losses from weather-related disasters totaled about $69 billion in 2007, an increase of 36 percent over the figure in 2006.[8] It is worth noting, however, that losses in 2006 were unusually low in comparison with losses in 2004 ($108 billion) and 2005 ($214 billion), when the hurricane seasons caused extraordinarily high economic and insured losses.[9] (See Figure 2.)

Fatalities due to weather-related disasters in 2007 (at 15,295) accounted for 95 percent of the deaths in all natural disasters.[10] This was an increase of 14 percent over fatalities in 2006.[11] More than half of the fatalities worldwide were caused by floods, 3 percent were from wet mass movements, 39 percent occurred in storm events, and 5 percent were during climatological events like extreme temperatures and wildfires.[12] (See Figure 3.)

The catastrophes with the greatest human tolls in 2007 occurred in developing and emerging countries. Storms, floods, and landslides in various parts of Asia caused more than 11,000 deaths, with some 3,300 attributable just to Cyclone Sidr, which struck Bangladesh in November.[13] In June, Cyclone Gonu crossed the Arabian Sea to Oman. It was the most intense storm ever recorded in the Arabian Sea and the heaviest tropical cyclone with a track leading into the Gulf of Oman.[14]

The number of named storms in the 2007 hurricane season (15) was much higher than the long-term climatological average of 10.6 named storms in 1950–2006 and roughly equal to the average of the current Atlantic warm phases.[15] Nevertheless, as only two of last year's hurricanes (Dean and Felix) were classified as intense storms, the intensity of the 2007 season was below the long-term average. At $60 million, economic losses in the United States for this hurricane season were far below average.[16]

But the United States suffered particularly from forest fires and heat waves in 2007. In California, hundreds of destructive wildland fires occurred from late October to early November.[17] Economic losses rose to $2.7 billion, while insured losses totaled $2.3 billion.[18] In August, central and southeastern parts of the United States were hit by a severe heat wave. It was the second warmest August since recording began 113 years ago.[19]

In November, the Mexican state of Tabasco and large parts of Chiapas suffered their most devastating floods in 50 years.[20] The Mexican authorities declared a state of emergency. About a million people were made homeless and lost all their possessions.[21]

Europe was also hit by natural catastrophes. Winter Storm Kyrill in January and two flood events in the United Kingdom in the summer were classified as "great natural disasters." Economic losses for these events were $18 billion and insured losses $12 billion.[22] Very high temperatures of up to 45 degrees Celsius (113 degrees Fahrenheit) and dryness for several months occurred in western Russia and southeastern Europe during the summer. Greece was

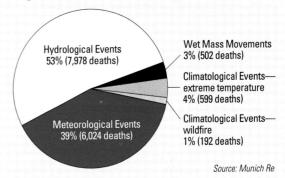

Figure 2. Economic and Insured Losses from Weather-Related Disasters, 1980–2007

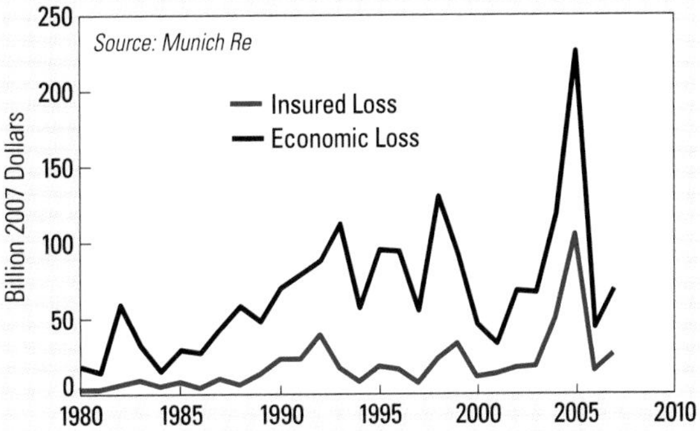

Source: Munich Re

Figure 3. Deaths from Weather-Related Disasters, 2007

Hydrological Events 53% (7,978 deaths)

Wet Mass Movements 3% (502 deaths)

Climatological Events— extreme temperature 4% (599 deaths)

Meteorological Events 39% (6,024 deaths)

Climatological Events— wildfire 1% (192 deaths)

Source: Munich Re

hit particularly hard by forest fires. Economic losses there reached $2 billion, the highest figure in Europe for decades.[23]

The main drivers for the recent increase in weather-related disasters and related global losses are socioeconomic factors and the changing patterns of extreme events.[24] The socioeconomic factors are tied to the rise in population, a better standard of living, the concentration of people and values in large urban settings, and the settlement and industrialization of regions with extremely high exposure levels.[25] Cities, metropolitan areas, and megacities are very vulnerable to natural catastrophes and especially to weather-related disasters. More than half of the world will be living in urban areas by the end of 2008.[26] And the urban population of developing and emerging countries is rising at an unprecedented rate. This is particularly noteworthy in Africa and Asia, where the urban population is expected to double between 2000 and 2030.[27]

The Fourth Assessment Report of the Intergovernmental Panel on Climate Change emphasizes the link between global warming and the significant likelihood of an increasing frequency and intensity of extreme weather events.[28] It is expected, with a more than 66 percent probability, that climate change will lead to warmer (and fewer cold) days and nights over land areas, more heat waves, heavier precipitation, and more areas affected by droughts and more-intense tropical cyclones—all of which could help increase the number of catastrophic weather events.[29]

Distribution of the impacts of weather-related disasters depends to a large degree on economic development in a country. Between 1980 and 2007, some 46 percent of all natural catastrophes but only 8 percent of the fatalities occurred in high-income countries.[30] Thus, 54 percent of the events hit middle-income and low-income countries, which suffered 92 percent of the fatalities.[31] Insurance penetration also depends on the development of the economy. Countries with a very low insurance penetration per capita are often low-income or lower-middle-income countries.[32] When weather-related disasters occur, international aid must be funded in an appropriate way for the countries involved. Protection against losses caused by disasters can be realized by such mechanisms as public-private partnerships for governments and micro-insurance solutions for private households.

The Caribbean Catastrophe Risk Insurance Facility (CCRIF) is one example of a public-private partnership that has proved highly successful. Founded in 2006 as an initiative of the World Bank, CCRIF offers 16 Caribbean countries financial assistance in the event of hurricanes and earthquakes.[33] Its purpose is to provide governments with index-based insurance against the losses caused by natural disasters. Private households can benefit from the implementation of micro-insurance solutions—one of several instruments designed to help people handle their personal risks a little better.

Global Economy and Resources Trends

© Vestas Wind Systems A/S

Maintenance worker on a wind turbine in Germany

For data and analysis on global economy and resources trends, go to www.worldwatch.org/vsonline.

Global Economic Growth Continues at Expense of Ecological Systems

Erik Assadourian

In 2007, gross world product (GWP)—the aggregated total of all finished goods and services produced worldwide—was expected to grow 5.4 percent to $72.3 trillion (in 2007 dollars).[1] (See Figure 1.) This estimate reflects actual purchasing power in countries (that is, in purchasing power parity or PPP terms). The market exchange rate GWP, which is based on straightforward monetary terms, was expected

Figure 1. Gross World Product, 1970–2007

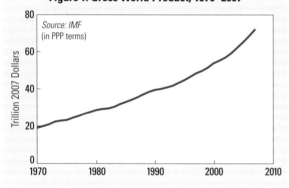

Source: IMF
(in PPP terms)

to reach $53.4 trillion, an increase of 8 percent since 2006.[2] The projected growth of GWP (PPP) in 2007 was revised downward from earlier estimates due particularly to economic disruptions in the U.S. housing market, which also had ripple effects in other countries, particularly within Europe and in Japan.[3] Even with this late-term contraction, growth in 2007 was still expected to be higher than the average since 1970.[4] (See Figure 2.)

The U.S. economy was projected to grow 2.1 percent in 2007, nearly 1 percent slower than the previous year.[5] This significant contraction came in large part from the turmoil felt in the subprime mortgage sector, with foreclosures,

reductions in residential investments, and declining housing values reducing growth as well as consumer confidence.[6] Rising gasoline prices also had a significant impact.[7] U.S. economic growth is expected to slow further in 2008.[8]

Although the U.S. economy still accounts for 19 percent of the world total, China is closing the gap—now accounting for 16 percent of GWP, up from 15 percent in 2006.[9] China's gross domestic product (GDP) grew dramatically in 2007, jumping an estimated 11.7 percent and making up one third of the projected $3.7 trillion in GWP growth in 2007.[10] Increases in exports and investments drove this expansion.[11]

Growth in China's GDP, however, has not come without cost. China is increasingly suffering from the externalities of economic growth: politically destabilizing inequality and pollution. Today, only 1 percent of China's 560 million urban residents breathe air that is considered safe by European Union (EU) standards.[12] Air and water pollution have led to numerous occurrences of social unrest.[13] And China is now the leading producer of sulfur dioxide emissions and has nearly surpassed the United States in total carbon dioxide emissions (though not in per capita emissions).[14]

The European Union now accounts for 21 percent of GWP, which as an aggregate makes it the largest economy in the world.[15] The EU economy was expected to grow 3.2 percent in 2007, having slowed in some countries due to investments in troubled U.S. financial markets.[16]

India's economy was expected to grow 9.1 percent in 2007, accounting for 11 percent of total GWP growth—more than the U.S. contribution.[17] Growth in the world's second most populous nation was mainly driven by domestic demand.[18]

Sub-Saharan Africa was projected to grow

6.1 percent—with this growth coming mostly from oil exports and from the dominant South African economy, which makes up one third of the region's gross product.[19] Although it is now growing more quickly than in the past, sub-Saharan Africa still accounts for just 2.6 percent of the global economy.[20]

Per capita GWP was expected to reach $10,956 in 2007.[21] (See Figure 3.) This was a growth of 4.1 percent—less than total GWP growth because world population increased by nearly 77 million people.[22] Yet GWP per capita does not reflect the vast disparity in GDP per person—even when these figures are expressed in purchasing power parity terms. In the United States, GDP per person is $44,974, for example, while in China the figure is $8,780 and in India it is just $4,183.[23]

Economic growth is having a direct impact on the ecological systems on which the human economy depends. As the U.N. Environmental Programme's recently published *Global Environmental Outlook–4* notes, human society is using the world's renewable resources unsustainably, thus degrading farmland and fisheries, rivers and forests.[24] And society is risking a significant weakening of the global economy if unsustainable resource use is not addressed. In particular, climate change could reduce economic growth by anywhere from 5 to 20 percent by 2100 if left unchecked.[25]

These warnings are not new. In 2005 the Millennium Ecosystem Assessment made it clear that nearly two thirds of ecosystem services have been degraded or are being used unsustainably, and indicators like the Ecological Footprint have demonstrated that human society has been living beyond its means since 1987.[26] According to this measure, humans are now using the equivalent of 1.25 planets' worth of resources.[27] (See Figure 4.) In short, without dramatic redesign of the global economy to reduce the ecological impacts, growth will most likely plummet—for instance, as extreme weather events disrupt agricultural production, flood coastal cities, and cause devastating wildfires.

Several analyses reveal that if ecological

Figure 2. Growth of Gross World Product, 1971–2007

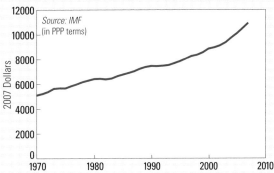

Figure 3. Gross World Product Per Person, 1970–2007

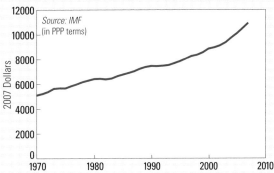

Figure 4. Humanity's Ecological Footprint, 1961–2003

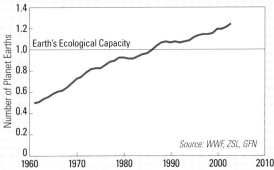

Figure 5. GDP and GPI Per Person, United States, 1950–2004

degradation is factored into economic calculations, true growth is much lower. In 2004, the Chinese government designed a Green GDP measure to subtract pollution costs from traditional GDP calculations.[28] The estimate for that year found that growth would have been 3.1 percent lower if these costs had been deducted.[29] Then in 2007, before releasing its 2005 analysis, the Chinese government shelved this indicator when it discovered that factoring in environmental costs would have reduced growth in some provinces to zero.[30]

GDP is a poor measure of actual economic progress, as it counts all monetary expenditures as positive—whether the money is spent on useful goods, such as food or durables, or on mitigating social ills that could have been prevented. In the United States, the nongovernmental organization Redefining Progress continues to track its Genuine Progress Indicator (GPI), a measure that provides a better analysis of economic progress by subtracting out pollution and resource degradation, crime, and other economic ills while adding in unmeasured benefits like volunteer work and parenting.[31] According to the most recent analysis, while U.S. GDP per capita nearly doubled since 1970, the GPI grew just 13 percent.[32] (See Figure 5.)

Recognizing that not all growth is good, some governments are starting to question whether economic growth should be a priority at all. Thailand, for example, has been investigating a transition to a "sufficiency economy," where the focus is on poverty alleviation (that is, targeted growth), economic self-reliance, and resource conservation.[33] While still in the theoretical stage, if some pioneering countries move toward this model, perhaps there will be a shift away from the unsustainable idea that infinite growth on a finite planet is a measure of economic success.

Carbon Markets Gain Momentum, Despite Challenges

Zoë Chafe

The global carbon market has expanded quickly over the past two years, buoyed by new and continued interest among national and regional governments in curbing carbon emissions. Worldwide, carbon trading reached a total value of $59.2 billion in 2007, up 80 percent over 2006, according to initial estimates from the market research group Point Carbon.[1] Earlier estimates indicated that the volume of carbon permits and credits traded in 2006 was more than double the amount traded in the previous year.[2] (See Table 1.)

Carbon markets are designed to combat climate change by putting a price on carbon dioxide (CO_2) and other greenhouse gases. Companies and other entities can trade the right to emit these gases through permits, credits, or allowances. The overall amount of emissions in a state or country is often limited by legislation. If a company emits more than allowed by law, it can buy permits from another company that has reduced its emissions to below its allocation.

In the past, large emitters (such as factories or power plants) had little financial incentive to limit carbon dioxide emissions because there were no costs directly associated with greenhouse gas emissions. Carbon markets are helping to internalize the true environmental costs of emitting CO_2 and other gases that contribute to climate change.

Mandatory carbon markets are underpinned by national or regional legislation. The European Union, for example, established the European Union Emissions Trading Scheme (EU-ETS) as part of its strategy to meet its Kyoto Protocol-mandated emissions targets.[3] With the EU-ETS, the European Union expects to meet its Kyoto targets for $4.3 billion–5.4 billion annually, an amount equivalent to less than 0.1 percent of the region's gross domestic product.[4] Without the EU-ETS, compliance costs would be about twice as high.[5]

The EU-ETS is the world's largest carbon trading platform. (See Figure 1.) Its test trading period began in 2005 and finished in 2007. During this time about 11,500 large emitters—such as power plants, heat generators, and energy-intensive factories—were included in the trading scheme. In 2006, the EU-ETS more than tripled the volume traded during the previous

Table 1. Carbon Transactions, Selected Markets, 2005 and 2006

Market	2005		2006	
	Volume	Value	Volume	Value
	(mill. tons of CO_2 equiv.)	(million 2007 dollars)	(mill. tons of CO_2 equiv.)	(million 2007 dollars)
EU Emissions Trading Scheme	321	8,351	1,101	24,936
New South Wales	6	62	20	230
Chicago Climate Exchange	1	3	10	39
Clean Development Mechanism	351	2,786	475	5,382
Joint Implementation	11	72	16	144
Other compliance	20	197	17	81
Other voluntary markets	6	n/a	13	56
TOTAL	716	11,471*	1,652	30,868

* Excludes over-the-counter voluntary market.

Source: World Bank, State and Trends of the Carbon Market 2007 (Washington, DC: May 2007), p. 3; Katherine Hamilton et al., State of the Voluntary Carbon Markets 2007: Picking Up Steam (San Francisco: Ecosystem Marketplace, July 2007).

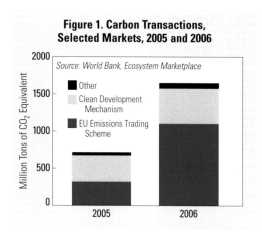

Figure 1. Carbon Transactions, Selected Markets, 2005 and 2006

Source: World Bank, Ecosystem Marketplace

- Other
- Clean Development Mechanism
- EU Emissions Trading Scheme

year, from 321 million tons of carbon dioxide equivalent to 1.1 billion tons.[6] (Carbon credits are measured in terms of CO_2 equivalent to account for the varying potential of carbon dioxide and other greenhouse gases to contribute to climate change.) The value of the traded carbon also tripled over the same time period, from $8.4 billion in 2005 to $24.9 billion in 2006 (in 2007 dollars).[7]

The EU-ETS entered its second trading phase in 2008. This phase, which lasts until 2012, corresponds to the Kyoto Protocol's first emissions reductions commitment period. New emissions sources, such as aviation, will be added, as will other types of greenhouse gases beyond carbon dioxide.[8] More stringent emissions caps during this period mean that there are fewer permits to be traded, and this is—so far—keeping prices higher than at the end of the first trading period. During 2007 there was an oversupply of permits, as too many had been initially allocated, and the price per permit crashed to nearly zero.[9] (See Figure 2.)

Other carbon credits can also be traded on the EU-ETS: those created through the Kyoto Protocol's "flexibility mechanisms." These are known as the Clean Development Mechanism (CDM) and Joint Implementation (JI). The CDM— which allows industrial countries to meet their Kyoto targets in part by investing in clean development projects in developing countries—pro-

duced 475 million tons of certified emissions reductions in 2006 alone.[10] These credits were valued at more than $5 billion.[11] JI, which has projects primarily in Eastern Europe, has been slower to start, with 16 million tons of credits traded in 2006, at a value of $144 million.[12]

Some observers are concerned that several important sources of greenhouse gases are not adequately addressed by the existing mechanisms. One area that has been especially controversial is known as Reducing Emissions from Deforestation in Developing Countries. With deforestation accounting for 20 percent of global emissions, including 70 percent of Brazil's emissions and 80 percent of Indonesia's, forest protection is an essential part of the efforts needed to combat climate change.[13] At climate negotiations in Bali in December 2007, the World Bank announced the creation of a Forest Carbon Partnership Facility.[14] This financial instrument is intended to compensate countries for costs they incur to keep existing forests intact.[15]

Forestry is often mentioned in conjunction with yet another type of carbon market: the voluntary market. This market is used by businesses, organizations, and individuals who voluntarily purchase carbon credits (often referred to as carbon offsets in this context) to mitigate their greenhouse gas emissions. The credits are usually exchanged over the counter—not through a formal market—or through an established trading mechanism such as the Chicago Climate Exchange (CCX). Ecosystem Marketplace, a U.S.-based organization that tracks environmental markets, estimated that in 2006 at least 23.7 million tons of CO_2 equivalent were exchanged on the voluntary market, including about 10.3 million tons exchanged through CCX.[16] The Chicago Climate Exchange reports that its trading volume doubled to 22.9 million tons during 2007.[17]

While carbon markets continue to grow, several key questions remain. One very important issue is whether and how the United States will establish a national carbon cap and will institute mandatory carbon trading. As the world's largest CO_2 emitter and the only industrial nation that has not ratified the Kyoto Protocol, the U.S. government's inaction threatens to mute the concerted efforts of the 176 other countries, and the European Union, that have ratified the protocol.[18]

In the meantime, several state and regional initiatives in the United States and Canada are gaining momentum. The Regional Greenhouse Gas Initiative (RGGI), which is set to begin in 2009, is a commitment by at least 10 northeastern states to cap regional CO_2 emissions at 1990 levels by 2014 and to reduce them by 10 percent below that level by 2018.[19] In 2006, California passed legislation requiring a 25-percent reduction in CO_2 emissions by 2020.[20] Carbon trading to meet this goal is likely to begin in 2012, and most reductions are expected to come from major emitters in-state.[21] And the Western Climate Initiative, modeled after RGGI, has set a goal of bringing regional emissions to 15 percent below 2005 levels by 2020 by establishing a market mechanism.[22] Currently, California, six other western states, and two Canadian provinces have signed on, with six other western states in the United States, one Mexican state, and three provinces joining as observers.[23]

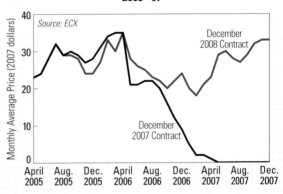

Figure 2. Average Price of EU Emissions Contracts, 2005–07

Jobs in Renewable Energy Expanding

Michael Renner

Driven by the gathering sense of a climate crisis, the notion of "green jobs"—especially in the renewable energy sector—is now receiving unprecedented attention. Currently about 2.3 million people worldwide work either directly in renewables or indirectly in supplier industries.[1] Given incomplete data, this is in all likelihood a conservative figure. The wind power industry employs some 300,000 people, the solar photovoltaics (PV) sector accounts for an estimated 170,000 jobs, and the solar thermal industry, at least 624,000.[2] More than 1 million jobs are found in the biomass and biofuels sector.[3] Small-scale hydropower and geothermal energy are far smaller employers. (See Figure 1.)

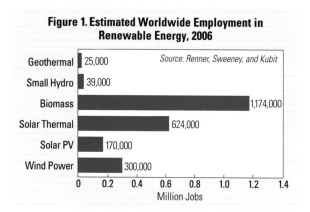

Figure 1. Estimated Worldwide Employment in Renewable Energy, 2006

Source: Renner, Sweeney, and Kubit

	Million Jobs
Geothermal	25,000
Small Hydro	39,000
Biomass	1,174,000
Solar Thermal	624,000
Solar PV	170,000
Wind Power	300,000

Renewables tend to be a more labor-intensive energy source than the still-dominant fossil fuels, which rely heavily on expensive pieces of production equipment. A transition toward renewables thus promises job gains. Even in the absence of such a transition, growing automation and corporate consolidation are already translating into steadily fewer jobs in the oil, natural gas, and coal industries—sometimes even in the face of expanding production. Many hundreds of thousands of coal mining jobs have been shed in China, the United States, Germany, the United Kingdom, and South Africa in the last decade or two.[4] In the United States, coal output rose by almost one third during the past two decades, yet employment has been cut in half.[5]

A handful of countries have emerged as leaders in renewables development, thanks to strong government support. A study commissioned by the German government found that in 2006 the country had some 259,000 direct and indirect jobs in the renewables sector.[6] The number is expected to reach 400,000–500,000 by 2020 and then 710,000 by 2030.[7]

Spain also has seen its renewables industry expand rapidly in recent years. The industry now employs some 89,000 people directly (mostly in wind power and PV) and another 99,000 indirectly.[8] Denmark has long been a leader in wind development. But with policy support there less steady in recent years, the number of domestic wind jobs has stagnated at about 21,000.[9]

In the United States, federal policies have been weak and inconsistent over the years, leaving leadership to individual state governments. Still, a study for the American Solar Energy Society found that the U.S. renewables sector employed close to 200,000 people directly in 2006 and another 246,000 indirectly.[10]

India's Suzlon is one of the world's leading wind turbine manufacturers, further strengthening its position through its 2007 takeover of Germany's REpower.[11] Manufacturing of wind turbine components, production of spare parts, and turbine maintenance by Suzlon and other companies are helping to generate much-needed income and employment in India.[12] Suzlon currently employs more than 13,000 people directly—about 10,000 in India, and the remainder in China, Belgium, and the United States.[13]

China is rapidly catching up in solar PVs and wind turbine manufacturing and is already the dominant force in solar hot water and small hydropower development.[14] According to rough estimates, close to a million people in China currently work in the renewables sector.[15] To some extent, these numbers reflect China's low labor productivity compared with Western countries. This seems especially true in the solar thermal industry, which is thought to employ some 600,000 people.[16]

The leaders in renewables technologies can expect considerable job gains in the near future in manufacturing solar panels and wind turbines for both domestic and export markets. Jobs in installing, operating, and maintaining renewable energy systems tend to be more local in nature and could thus benefit a broad range of countries.

For instance, Kenya has one of the largest and most dynamic solar markets in the developing world. There are 10 major solar PV import companies, and the country has an estimated 1,000– 2,000 solar technicians.[17] In Bangladesh, Grameen Shakti has installed more than 100,000 solar home systems in rural communities in a few years—one of the fastest-growing solar PV programs in the world—and is aiming for 1 million by 2015, along with the creation of some 100,000 jobs for local youth and women as solar technicians and repair and maintenance specialists.[18]

Four countries—Brazil, the United States, China, and Germany—are leading in biomass development. Brazil's ethanol industry is said to employ about 300,000 workers.[19] Indonesia and Malaysia are leading palm oil producers; a small but growing share is being diverted there to biofuels production. Malaysia has an estimated half-million people employed in the palm oil industry (and another million people whose livelihoods are connected to it)—many of them Indonesian migrant workers.[20] Indonesia is itself planning a major expansion, and optimistic projections speak of 3.5 million new plantation jobs by 2010.[21]

Following a wave of initial enthusiasm, there are now rising doubts about the environmental benefits and economic impacts of at least some types of biofuels, however.[22] And the jobs that are being created need close scrutiny as well. Biofuels processing typically requires higher skills and thus is likely to offer better pay than feedstock production and harvesting. But most jobs are found at sugarcane and palm oil plantations, where wages and working conditions are often extremely poor.

The Brazilian sugarcane industry has historically been marked by exploitation of seasonal laborers and by the takeover of smaller-scale farms by large plantation owners, often by violent means.[23] The prevailing piece-rate system leaves many Brazilian plantation workers earning a pittance, and some end up in debt bondage. Living conditions are often squalid.[24] In Indonesia, too, poverty is common among plantation workers, who face unsafe working conditions, frequent denial of their rights, and intimidation by employers.[25]

The expansion of plantations for biofuels also threatens to come at the expense of rural jobs and rural communities. Oil palm companies seeking to acquire land in Indonesia's West Kalimantan, for example, have been found to hold out false promises of jobs for local communities.[26] A 2006 study of the area found that small farming systems provided livelihoods for 260 times as many people per hectare of land as oil palm plantations did.[27]

According to the Woods Hole Research Center, India could create some 900,000 jobs by 2025 in biomass gasification.[28] Of this total, 300,000 jobs would be with manufacturers of gasifier stoves (including masons, metal fabricators, and so on) and 600,000 would be in biomass production, processing into briquettes and pellets, supply chain operations, and after-sales services.[29] Another 150,000 people might find employment in advanced biomass cooking technologies.[30]

While biofuels are now subject to more critical reviews on a number of fronts, the future looks promising for wind and solar. *Global Wind*

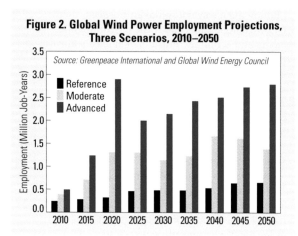

Figure 2. Global Wind Power Employment Projections, Three Scenarios, 2010–2050

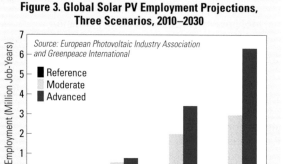

Figure 3. Global Solar PV Employment Projections, Three Scenarios, 2010–2030

Energy Outlook 2006 outlines three scenarios—conservative, moderate, and advanced—for future worldwide wind energy development, assuming different rates of investments and capacity expansion.[31] (See Figure 2.) Global wind power employment is projected to grow to as much as 2.1 million in 2030 and 2.8 million in 2050 under the advanced scenario.[32] *Solar Generation IV*, a 2007 report by the European Photovoltaic Industry Association and Greenpeace International, similarly projects worldwide solar PV developments via three scenarios.[33] By 2030, as many as 6.3 million jobs could be created under the best case scenario.[34] (See Figure 3.)

Expanding the role of renewables helps make other sectors of the economy, such as transportation and buildings, more sustainable—thus greening additional jobs to some degree.

Microfinance Surging

Gary Gardner

The number of "microborrowers" worldwide increased by 17 percent in 2006, according to data from the Microcredit Summit Campaign, continuing double-digit annual growth that averaged some 29 percent annually between 2001 and 2006.[1] (See Figure 1.) The global loan portfolio of the 340 microfinance institutions (MFIs) tracked by the Microfinance Information Exchange (MIX) also grew rapidly in 2006, at some 34 percent.[2] (See Table 1.) The galloping advance of microcredit is increasing pressure on many MFIs to become more sophisticated and commercially oriented in their operations—at the expense, some analysts fear, of their original mission of poverty reduction.[3]

Microfinance refers to financial services, including loans, savings accounts, and insurance products, that are designed to serve people with very low incomes. The average microloan size worldwide is now $1,026 and the average savings account balance is $1,126.[4] Globally, the loan write-off ratio was 3.1 percent in 2006—a better record than that of many commercial banks.[5] Women are a key clientele of most microfinance programs, accounting for 98 percent of borrowers in Asia and some two thirds of clients in Africa, Latin America, and the Middle East.[6] Only in Eastern Europe and Central Asia are women a minority of customers; there, some 47 percent of borrowers are women.[7]

As the birthplace of microfinance, Asia leads the world in total current borrowers, with nearly 113 million—some 85 percent of the global total.[8] (See Table 2.) Latin America reported the fastest growth in borrowers in 2006, at 53 percent.[9] This region also has the largest overall loan portfolio, while Eastern Europe and Central Asia report the largest average loan balance per borrower.

The potential of microfinance to reduce poverty and to succeed commercially has attracted growing amounts of foreign investment. Between 2004 and 2006, foreign capital investment in microfinance more than tripled globally, to $4 billion.[10] Some 75 percent of this investment went to 30 countries in Latin America and in Eastern Europe and Central Asia.[11] Africa and Asia, which are poorer and arguably would benefit more from microfinance, received only 6 and 7 percent respectively.[12]

Investment from development finance institu-

Figure 1. Microcredit Clients Worldwide, 1997–2006

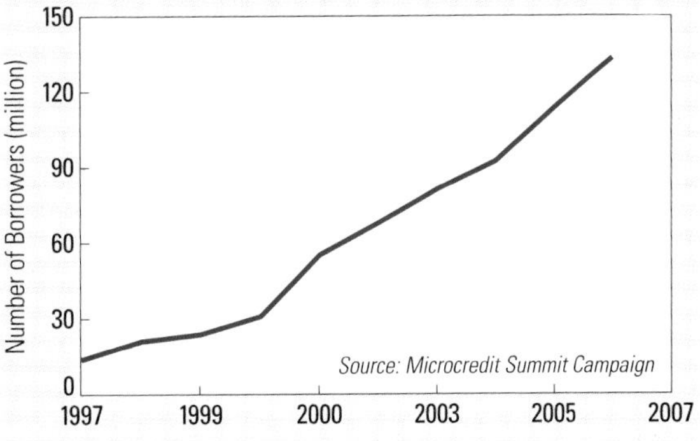

Source: Microcredit Summit Campaign

Table 1. Growth in Microloans and Microsavings, 2004–06

Indicator	2004	2006	Annual Growth
	(million dollars)		(compounded, percent)
Loan portfolio	7,501	13,524	34
Total savings deposits	6,406	9,803	24

Note: Figures based on mean data from 340 microfinance institutions tracked by Microfinance Information Exchange. Source: See endnote 2.

Table 2. Selected Microfinance Indicators, by Region, 2006

Region	Number of Current Borrowers	Gross Loan Portfolio	Average Loan Balance per Borrower
	(million)	(million)	(dollars)
Africa	8.4	1,371	516
Asia	112.7	6,971	371
Eastern Europe and Central Asia	3.4	4,636	2,424
Latin America and the Caribbean	6.8	9,668	1,148
Middle East and North Africa	1.7	64	631
North America and Western Europe	0.05	—	—

Note: Data on number of current borrowers are drawn from a different database than data on gross loan portfolio and average loan balance, so they should not be used in conjunction with loan data to draw further conclusions.
Source: See endnote 8.

tions (DFIs)—public monies from governments and intergovernmental organizations—jumped from $1 billion in 2004 to $2.5 billion in 2006 and now accounts for just over half of foreign investment in microfinance.[13] DFIs include institutions such as the International Finance Corporation of the World Bank, the Inter-American Development Bank, KfW in Germany, and the Overseas Private Investment Corporation in the United States. These institutions brought a commercial approach to microfinance, but they did so on flexible terms and with low interest rates that helped to build and strengthen the industry.[14]

Commercial institutions such as investment banks and private equity firms are investing in microfinance in expectation of high returns. The concern surrounding involvement of these institutions is that they may pressure MFIs to act more like commercial firms, for example by distributing profits to shareholders rather than reinvesting them in microfinance activities or by charging the highest possible interest rate to create the greatest financial return, even if it dilutes the social return.[15] Proponents of private investment counter that commercializing microfinance is needed to attract the large sums of capital that allow it to spread rapidly.[16]

The commercialization debate was highlighted most dramatically in 2007 when Compartamos Banco, a Mexican MFI, became a publicly traded corporate bank offering a full range of financial services to the poor.[17] Its initial public offering raised more than $450 million and drew 13 times more bids for shares than could be accommodated.[18] Compartamos Banco's popularity among investors is a direct function of its profitability, which in turn stems from its relatively high interest rates—roughly 83 percent.[19] This is comparable to other Mexican MFIs but well above the 30–50 percent levied in many other countries.[20] Microfinance practitioners, investors, and analysts are engaged in a fierce debate regarding the validity of the Compartamos model for microfinance as a whole.

Critics maintain that the high interest rates gouge the poor and put poverty alleviation goals—traditionally the core of microfinance—on the back burner. Mohammed Yunus, winner of the 2006 Nobel Peace Prize for pioneering work in microfinance, describes the Compartamos business model as "not consistent with microcredit" and argues that interest rates should be kept "as close to the cost of funds as possible."[21] Proponents counter that Compartamos's rates fall within the range charged by many lending institutions in Mexico, are justified by the expense associated with tiny loans, and in any case are affordable—as the high repayment rate attests.[22] They also argue that Compartamos plows a large share of profits back into the bank (rather than to shareholders), allowing for rapid expansion of lending to poor borrowers.[23] Critics countercharge that capital for expansion could come from promoting savings among the poor, even if this meant slower rates of growth in microfinance.[24]

An intriguing innovation that could stimulate growth in microfinance is "branchless banking"—the use of mobile phones or a decentralized network of small retail shops for deposits and withdrawals. Retail outlets are already used for microbanking in Brazil, while mobile phones are in use in the Philippines.[25] Both methods are thought to offer major cost savings for banks. In Pakistan, the setup cost of a conventional bank branch is estimated to be 30 times greater than the cost of contracting with a shopkeeper.[26] And in the Philippines, where a conventional banking transaction costs $2.50, an automated transaction using a mobile phone is estimated to cost only 50¢.[27] Neither mobile phone banking nor banking at retail outlets is easy to establish, however, and it remains to be seen whether branchless banking can become a mainstream financial services outlet for the poor.

The potential for expansion of microfinance could be significant. Today's 133 million microborrowers represent only 5 percent of the people living on $2 or less per day in 2001.[28] Many of the unserved may not want a microloan or may not qualify for one, of course, but the experience of Bangladesh suggests that microfinance can penetrate deeply: some 62–75 percent of eligible Bangladeshis have had a microloan.[29] On the other hand, Bangladesh may be exceptional; other mature microcredit markets, such as Bolivia's, have much more modest penetration rates.[30] In any case, the Microcredit Summit Campaign, whose goal of recruiting 100 million borrowers between 1997 and 2005 spurred the surge in microfinance, is now working to expand the number of microcredit recipients to 175 million by 2015.[31]

The future of microfinance depends in part on how the industry handles the new challenges created by rapid growth. A 2008 survey of microfinance practitioners, investors, and analysts by the Centre for the Study of Financial Innovation identified 20 risks that could derail the advance of microfinance.[32] Six of the top 10 were management risks: management quality, corporate governance, cost control, staffing, technology management, and credit risk management.[33] MFIs lacking strong management skills may find it difficult to run a successful firm if their operations expand rapidly and become more complex.

Population and Society Trends

Aron Kremer

Families picnic in a Tokyo park

For data and analysis on population and society trends, go to www.worldwatch.org/vsonline.

Peacekeeping Budgets and Personnel
Soar to New Heights

Michael Renner

Costs for United Nations peacekeeping operations from July 2007 to June 2008 are expected to run to $7 billion—substantially higher than the record $5.6 billion spent in 2006–07.[1] (See Figure 1.) Currently running operations in 17 countries, the United Nations now deploys more soldiers, military observers, and police than ever before: a total of 84,309 as of December 2007.[2] (See Figure 2.) This figure includes more than 70,000 soldiers, close to 10,000 police, and about 2,500 military observers.[3] Counting international and local civilian staff and volunteers, the total runs up to about 106,000.[4] And 11 smaller "political and peacebuilding" missions (typically follow-up efforts once a peacekeeping mission ends) deployed another 3,787 personnel as of late 2007.[5] Of the total U.N. personnel, about 7,000 are women—2,000 in uniform and 5,000 civilians.[6]

Figure 1. U.N. Peacekeeping Expenditures, 1950–2007

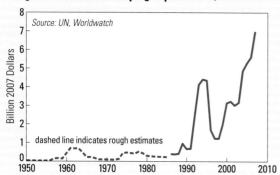

Still, U.N. peacekeeping continues to be dwarfed by military spending and staffing priorities. World military budgets stood at $1,232 billion in 2006—that's 228 times as much as was spent on U.N. peacekeeping.[7] The extended U.S. war in Iraq has cost about $632 billion, or an average of more than $100 billion per year.[8] International deployments of national military forces that are not part of peacekeeping operations totaled about 540,000 in 2005.[9] U.S. troops in Iraq, Afghanistan, and other military bases around the globe account for about 394,000 of that figure.[10] Other countries with significant foreign deployments—Turkey, the United Kingdom, France, Russia—together have about 117,000 soldiers in other countries.[11]

Two new U.N. missions were authorized during 2007: UNAMID, a U.N.–African Union "hybrid" force in Darfur, and MINURCAT, a mission in the Central African Republic (CAR) and Chad. This region of Africa is home to a series of partially linked crises. Instability and violence in Sudan's Darfur region have spilled over into neighboring Chad, which is also suffering from clashes between the government and two rebel groups along the border with Sudan. And in the CAR, fighting persists in the northwest and along the border with Chad and Cameroon.[12]

A U.N. Security Council resolution passed in July 2007 authorized UNAMID to grow to nearly 20,000 military personnel, plus several thousand police officers and civilians.[13] But these numbers won't be reached until perhaps late 2008. Aid workers fear that in the meantime the humanitarian situation for millions of displaced people will not improve.[14]

Peacekeepers come from all corners of the world. Altogether, 119 countries contributed personnel to the U.N. missions in 2007—including many nations that themselves suffer from armed conflict.[15] During 1996–2007, Bangladesh, India, Nepal, Pakistan, and Sri Lanka accounted for 34 percent of the total.[16] Five other nations each provided more than

2,000 peacekeepers: Ghana, Jordan, Italy, Nigeria, and Uruguay.[17] Eleven additional countries, more than half of them African, made at least 1,000 peacekeepers available.[18] Stepped-up commitments by China and France brought the contribution of five permanent members of the Security Council to close to 6 percent of all personnel.[19] Yet at about 300 personnel each, the other three permanent members—the United States, United Kingdom, and Russia—remained stingy contributors, especially relative to their own military engagements around the world.[20]

Seven missions account for about 87 percent of the current peacekeeping budget.[21] Missions in the Democratic Republic of the Congo and in southern Sudan together cost more than $2 billion in 2007–08, and the new mission in Darfur alone is pegged at close to $1.5 billion, pending U.N. General Assembly budgetary approval.[22] The next four largest deployments—in Liberia, Haiti, Côte d'Ivoire, and Lebanon—together cost about $2.5 billion.[23] The top missions also account for the bulk of all currently deployed U.N. peacekeeping personnel.[24]

Two thirds of all Blue Helmets, as U.N. peacekeepers are called, are currently deployed in nine missions in Africa (and that portion is set to expand as UNAMID's ranks swell toward authorized deployment limits).[25] The Middle East has the second most, with 16 percent, followed by the Americas with 11 percent, Europe with 6 percent, and Asia with 3 percent.[26]

Compared with the early days of peacekeeping—when missions were largely limited to monitoring and maintaining peace along well-defined lines and were based on strict neutrality—today's missions are highly complex. They often involve providing assistance in elections and other political processes, building or rebuilding institutions, reforming judicial systems, training law enforcement and police forces, disarming and reintegrating former combatants, and performing other tasks that help foster and consolidate peace.[27] In a number of cases, such as Cambodia, East Timor, and Kosovo, the United Nations even acted as the transitional authority in the absence of a recog-

Figure 2. U.N. Peacekeeping Personnel, 1950–2007

Source: Global Policy Forum, UN, Stimson Center

nized or functioning government.[28]

The Security Council approves new missions but does not necessarily see to it that they have the necessary resources, leading to growing strains.[29] One bottleneck is the limited capacity or willingness of member states to provide adequately trained personnel and equipment in a timely manner, which has led to delayed deployments and overburdened peacekeepers.

To pay for peacekeeping, member states are assessed a portion of the total costs according to a formula measuring their ability to pay. The top two—the United States and Japan—together are responsible for 43 percent of the total bill.[30] Germany, the United Kingdom, and France account for 24 percent.[31] Overall, just 15 countries cover 90 percent of the budget.[32] But when they balk, by paying late or withholding part of what they owe, peacekeeping finances are thrown into deep crisis, as has happened repeatedly.

As of November 2007, $3.15 billion of peacekeeping payments had not been made by national governments.[33] (See Figure 3.) At $1.1 billion, the United States owed 34 percent of this total.[34] Japan is the number two deadbeat (at $730 million), followed by France ($189 million) and China ($178 million).[35] The next 11 largest contributors together owed another $454 million. Only Mexico and Brazil came close to paying their dues in full.[36]

Nowadays the United Nations is far from the

Figure 3. Arrears of U.N. Members for Peacekeeping Expenses, 1975–2007

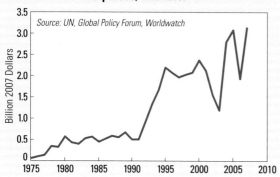

Figure 4. Personnel of Non-U.N. Peacekeeping Missions, 1976–2007

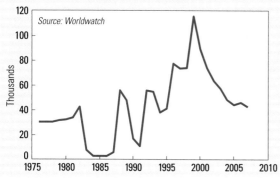

only organization that dispatches peacekeepers. Non-U.N. missions can also be found in all regions of the world, often with the imprimatur of the U.N. Security Council (and thus added legitimacy) and sometimes working as "hybrids" in conjunction with the Blue Helmets. Indeed, in some conflict areas multiple missions are deployed simultaneously.

During 2007, 47 missions were maintained by a variety of regional organizations, such as the European Union and the Organization for Security and Co-operation in Europe, or by ad hoc coalitions.[37] They involved an estimated 42,000 soldiers in 2007.[38] (See Figure 4.) Budget information is incomplete, but these deployments cost at least $1.3 billion in 2007.[39] And these data exclude the 41,000-plus soldiers of the NATO-led International Security Assistance Force, as this increasingly resembles conventional combat more than peacekeeping.[40]

For both U.N. and non-U.N. missions there are lingering questions about how to deal with situations where there may not be any peace to be kept. Mandates now often include "peace enforcement" by force of arms—a product of criticism that earlier missions were ineffective and of the growing acceptance of a "responsibility to protect" civilian populations who are in harm's way. But there is always a danger that peacekeepers become just another warring party.

Fertility Falls, Population Rises, Future Uncertain

Robert Engelman

Although the average woman worldwide is giving birth to fewer children than ever before (see Figure 1), an estimated 136 million babies were born in 2007.[1] Global data do not allow demographers to be certain that any specific year sets a record for births, but this one certainly came close. The year's cohort of babies propelled global population to an estimated 6.7 billion by the end of 2007. (See Figure 2.)

The seeming contradiction between smaller-than-ever families and near-record births is easily explained. The number of women of childbearing age keeps growing and global life expectancy at birth continues to rise. These two trends explain why population continues growing despite declines in family size. There were 1.7 billion women aged 15 to 49 in late 2007, compared with 856 million in 1970. The average human being born today can expect to live 67 years, a full decade longer than the average newborn could expect in 1970.

Only the future growth of the reproductive-age population is readily predictable, however: all but the youngest of the women who will be in this age group in two decades are already alive today. But sustaining further declines in childbearing and increases in life expectancy will require continued efforts by governments to improve access to good health care, and both trends could be threatened by environmental or social deterioration. The uncertain future of these factors makes population growth harder to predict than most people realize.

Diversity in fertility rates (the average number of children born to each woman) and life expectancy (the years that the average baby born today can be expected to live) marks the world's population in the early twenty-first century. Women typically bear five or six children in parts of sub-Saharan Africa and western Asia,

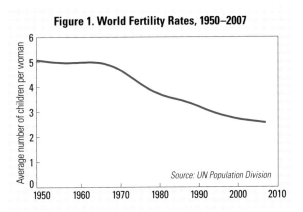

Figure 1. World Fertility Rates, 1950–2007

Average number of children per woman

Source: UN Population Division

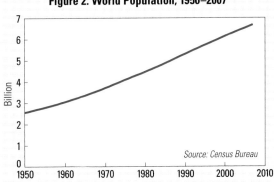

Figure 2. World Population, 1950–2007

Billion

Source: Census Bureau

while women have fewer than two in most industrial countries and some developing ones, such as Cuba, Sri Lanka, Thailand, and Tunisia.

Fertility rates that were consistently below two children per woman would eventually lead to a shrinkage of national populations in the absence of counterbalancing immigration. It can take decades for low fertility to halt growth, however, in populations with large proportions

Figure 3. Correlation Between Status of Women and National Fertility Rates

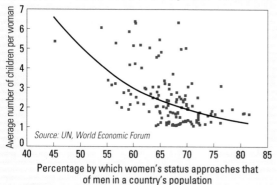

Source: UN, World Economic Forum

Percentage by which women's status approaches that of men in a country's population

Average number of children per woman

Note: The dots place countries according to their total fertility rate and their score on an index of women's status as a percentage of men's. As the regression curve averaging the countries' positions shows, higher women's status correlates with smaller families. At the high end of women's status, fertility rates are close to the "replacement" fertility rate of about two children per woman.

of young people due to high fertility in the past.

Life expectancy worldwide varies from a high of 83 years in Japan to a low of 40 years in Swaziland, the country with the highest prevalence of HIV infection. Worldwide, deaths from AIDS totaled approximately 2.1 million in 2007, and even more people—some 2.5 million—are estimated to have been newly infected with HIV that year.[2] One bright sign is that in 2007 the Joint United Nations Programme on HIV/AIDS and the World Health Organization lowered their estimates of HIV infections worldwide, from approximately 39 million to 33 million.[3] But this represented a statistical adjustment, not a downward trend in infections.

Due to both the unprecedented number of people alive and the ease of travel, the global movement of people has continued on the largest scale in history. Data are insufficient, however, to be confident about trends from one year to the next. The United Nations estimated that in 2005 nearly 200 million people lived outside their country of birth, a "nation" of international migrants as large as Brazil—and twice as many people as were in that category in 1980.[4]

U.N. demographers believe that the numbers of people moving to other countries to work and live is rising, propelled by increases in undocumented international migration and in refugees returning to their home countries.[5] Many more people move within countries. By the end of 2008, half of the world is expected for the first time in human history to live in such urban areas—though since the definition of "urban" varies by country, there is no way to be certain when this moment of global rural-urban equilibrium actually occurs.[6]

The United States adds to global demographic diversity by having by far the largest population in the industrial world (about 303 million) and average fertility above two children per woman, the highest among industrial countries.[7] In 2006, U.S. fertility rose to its highest rate since 1971—2.1 children per woman.[8] Among the reasons for the jump may be decreasing access to abortion and greater proportions of young people lacking easy and affordable access to sexuality education and contraception. Although this level of fertility could eventually stabilize an industrial country's population if there were no net immigration, in the United States the proportions not only of immigrants but of young women of childbearing age are both so high that no such outcome is imminent.

Among the most direct influences on fertility is access to and use of contraception. More than 700 million women, half of those aged 15 to 49 in developing countries, are at risk of unintended pregnancy, due to either improper use of contraception or—for an estimated 137 million women—no use of contraception at all.[9] At the same time, spending on family planning by governments worldwide has been stagnant in recent years—and has remained at a fraction of what governments agreed is needed to assure all women and couples access to services and contraceptives.[10]

A trend that may be more hopeful for the future of world population is the gradual improvement worldwide of women's health and their economic, educational, and political status relative to men. For the past two years the World Economic Forum (WEF) has assembled a global index of the closing of this gender gap. The 2007 index showed slight improvements over 2006 in every category except health.[11] A comparison of the percent of the overall gender gap that had closed and the fertility rates of 128 countries indicated a clear correlation between high female status and low fertility.[12] (See Figure 3.) The new WEF index could provide a dataset worth watching in the years ahead, and—if the gender gap continues narrowing—could point the way toward a more environmentally sustainable and socially equal human population in the years ahead.

Child Mortality Drops Below 10 Million

Hannah Doherty

In 2006, the latest year with data available, the world's child mortality rate—the number of children who die before the age of five per 1,000 live births—dropped to 72, a 20-percent decline since 1990, when 93 children died for every 1,000 live births.[1] (See Figure 1.) For the first time since recordkeeping began in 1960, child mortality fell below 10 million, to 9.7 million, which was less than half the number who died before reaching five in 1960.[2] This welcome achievement, however, still leaves most developing countries well short of the pace needed to meet the United Nations Millennium Development Goal (MDG) of reducing under-five child mortality by two thirds between 1990 and 2015. And despite the steady decline in global under-five deaths, disparities between and within regions continue to grow.

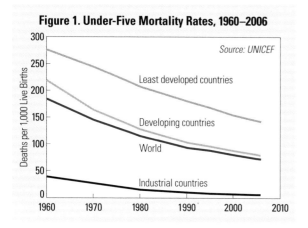

Figure 1. Under-Five Mortality Rates, 1960–2006

Source: UNICEF

Least developed countries

Developing countries

World

Industrial countries

Under-five mortality decreases as per capita income increases.[3] In the poorest households in developing countries, 107 children under the age of five die for every 1,000 live births.[4] This is nearly 40 percent higher than in the richest households in those nations, where the rate is 67 deaths for every 1,000 live births.[5] The disparity is even greater when compared with the rate in industrial nations—6 deaths per 1,000 live births.[6]

For the average child living in rural areas and isolated from basic health services and adequate sanitation, the under-five mortality rate is 105—far greater than in urban areas, where the rate is 69 deaths per 1,000 live births.[7]

East Asia and the Pacific, Central and Eastern Europe, and Latin America and the Caribbean have reduced child mortality rates by half since 1990.[8] (See Figure 2.) They are the only regions on track to meet the child mortality MDG.[9] In 2006, the mortality rate for each of these regions was below 30 per 1,000 live births.[10]

A number of countries in Latin America, such as Cuba and Chile, have lowered their child mortality rates by more than 50 percent since 1990 and are more than halfway to cutting them by two thirds.[11] Despite these positive trends, the averages mask wide disparities between and within Latin America.[12] The mortality rates of Haiti and Bolivia are more than twice the regional average, and indigenous children living in both urban and rural areas in Latin America face a greater risk of dying before their first birthday than non-indigenous children.[13]

South Asia has shown improvement, reducing its under-five mortality rate from 123 child deaths per 1,000 live births in 1990 to 83 in 2006.[14] Even with the improvements, however, in 2006 this region had the second highest number of deaths among children under the age of five—roughly 3.1 million—accounting for 32 percent of the global total.[15]

Afghanistan, Pakistan, and India account for half the world's undernourished children, despite having just 29 percent of the developing world's under-five population.[16] Afghanistan's child mortality rate was 252 for the 2002–05 period, three times South Asia's average rate and the third highest in the world.[17] Compared with the regional average of 1 child death for every 12 children, in Afghanistan 1 child dies for every 5 children.[18]

Sub-Saharan Africa has made the least progress in reducing child mortality rates, with 1 in every 6 children dying before the age of five.[19] On average, its under-five mortality rate was 160 deaths for every 1,000 live births in 2006, an improvement from its 1990 rate of 187.[20] Some countries in West and Central Africa, however, have made no progress, and some nations actually reported increases in under-five mortality rates, such as Côte d'Ivoire.[21] Only 22 percent of the world's children are born in sub-Saharan Africa, yet this region accounts for 49 percent of the world's under-five deaths.[22]

Lack of safe water and sanitation along with inadequate hygiene are largely responsible for breeding the leading killers of children under five: diarrheal diseases, pneumonia, neonatal disorders, and undernutrition.[23] Some 88 percent of diarrheal diseases, the second most common direct cause of under-five deaths, are attributed to poor water management.[24] These illnesses take nearly 2 million children a year and account for 17 percent of children deaths.[25]

Access to adequate health care is also a leading contributor. Pneumonia, the single leading cause of child mortality, kills 2 million children and 1 million infants worldwide each year, accounting for 19 percent of children's deaths and nearly a quarter of neonatal deaths.[26] Sadly, only 56 percent of the world's children with pneumonia are taken to appropriate health care providers.[27]

Life is most vulnerable in the first 28 days of life, when most of the world's child deaths occur, taking 4 million infants each year.[28] Collectively, neonatal causes contribute to 37 percent of under-five deaths. The disparity between neonatal deaths in rich and poor nations has been growing.[29] Newborns in developing countries are eight times more likely than newborns

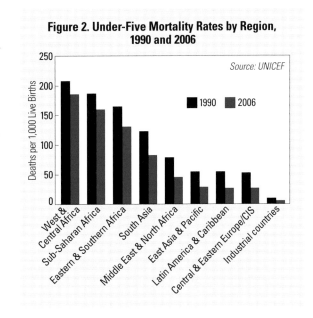

Figure 2. Under-Five Mortality Rates by Region, 1990 and 2006

in industrial countries to die, largely because mothers there receive inadequate or no care during pregnancy, childbirth, and the postpartum period.[30] The World Health Organization reports that nearly three quarters of all neonatal deaths could be prevented if women were adequately nourished and received appropriate care.[31] Skilled help at birth can prevent the leading causes of newborn deaths—severe infections and asphyxia, which together account for 49 percent of neonatal deaths.[32]

Undernutrition, the result of insufficient food intake and repeated infectious diseases, decreases a child's resistance to infection and is the underlying cause in up to half of all under-five deaths.[33] With 42 percent of South Asia's under-five population underweight, the region has the highest rate of undernutrition worldwide.[34] Maternal undernutrition is also a significant contributing factor to child mortality, leading to children who are severely underweight with stunted physical and intellectual growth.[35]

The low status of women presents serious challenges in reducing child mortality, especially in South Asia and sub-Saharan Africa. In India, for example, girls are up to 50 percent more likely than boys to die between their first and fifth birthdays.[36] Exclusion of girls from health care is often most severe in rural areas and in urban slums, where women are largely illiterate and suffer from sociocultural barriers to services, compromising the health of all family members.[37] Poverty, race, language, and culture are other factors excluding women and their children from public health services.[38]

Armed conflicts and AIDS also affect a young child's prospects for survival. More than half of the 11 countries where 20 percent or more of children die before age five suffered a major armed conflict since 1989.[39] In the war-torn Democratic Republic of Congo, for example, the child mortality rate was 211 per 1,000 live births in 2000–05.[40] AIDS has also destabilized sub-Saharan Africa, leaving 12 million children without parents.[41] A motherless child is more likely than an infant with a surviving mother to die before reaching age two.[42] And the children themselves are dying of AIDS: sub-Saharan Africa accounts for almost 90 percent of pediatric HIV infections.[43]

The MDG campaign has encouraged basic health interventions, such as early and exclusive breastfeeding, measles immunization, and Vitamin A supplementation, which have decreased child mortality rates.[44] In Latin America, timely measles immunization since 2000 has reached 93 percent of the region's population, nearly eliminating this disease that still kills at least 1 million people a year, 80 percent of whom are children under the age of five.[45]

If the MDG is to be reached, annual child mortality must be reduced to fewer than 5 million by 2015.[46] Achieving this will rely heavily on accomplishing the other important Millennium Development Goals: reducing poverty and hunger, improving maternal health, increasing the use of cleaner water and sanitation, and providing affordable essential drugs on a sustainable basis.

Environment a Growing Driver
in Displacement of People

Michael Renner

The number of people who are on the move involuntarily worldwide may be as high as 184 million—roughly equivalent to the entire population of Brazil, or one out of every 36 persons on Earth.[1] Among them are 16 million refugees (including 4.6 million Palestinians) and 26 million internally displaced people (IDPs—those who, unlike refugees, did not cross an international border).[2] (See Figures 1 and 2.) Another 12 million people are stateless—they are vulnerable because they lack the protection of citizenship, although they are not necessarily displaced.[3] Some 25 million people have been uprooted by natural disasters.[4] And Christian Aid, a London-based advocacy group, estimates that as many as 105 million people are made homeless by a variety of so-called development projects, including dams, mines, roads, factories, plantations, and wildlife reserves.[5]

Because these estimates come from different sources, the total of 184 million needs to be regarded with some caution. This is especially so because the Christian Aid figure is a rough estimate and may partially overlap with the other categories.

Environmental and resource pressures are increasingly a driver of displacement. They also have an impact on the number of long-term migrants—people who leave voluntarily and live outside their home country for a year or longer—whose numbers rose from 75 million in 1965 to some 200 million in 2005.[6] In relative terms, however, the number of long-term migrants has remained at roughly 2–3 percent of global population.[7]

The U.N. High Commissioner for Refugees (UNHCR) has traditionally been tasked with assisting those who seek refuge from war and repression. The largest groups of refugees under UNHCR's care in 2007 were 3 million Afghanis

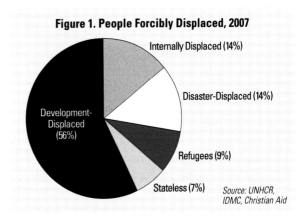

Figure 1. People Forcibly Displaced, 2007

Internally Displaced (14%)

Disaster-Displaced (14%)

Development-Displaced (56%)

Refugees (9%)

Stateless (7%)   *Source: UNHCR, IDMC, Christian Aid*

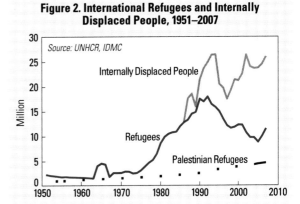

Figure 2. International Refugees and Internally Displaced People, 1951–2007

Source: UNHCR, IDMC

Internally Displaced People

Refugees

Palestinian Refugees

(mostly residing in Pakistan and Iran) and 2 million Iraqis (mainly in Syria and Jordan).[8] UNHCR also helped Colombians (552,000), Sudanese (523,000), and Somalis (457,000).[9] (A separate agency, the United Nations Relief and Works Agency for Palestine Refugees in the Near East, or UNRWA, is responsible for Palestinian refugees, who number 4.6 million.)[10] In

2007, Sudan was the country with the highest number of IDPs (5.8 million), followed by Colombia (up to 4 million), Iraq (2.5 million), the Democratic Republic of the Congo (1.4 million), and Uganda (1.3 million).[11]

According to U.N. High Commissioner for Refugees Antonio Guterres, it will be increasingly difficult to easily categorize the displaced by separate causes.[12] Environmental degradation, for example, is now often seen to be a factor contributing to both involuntary and voluntary population movements. But environmental problems are often closely intertwined with socioeconomic conditions (poverty, inequality of land ownership, etc.), resource disputes, and poor governance.[13]

The concept of "environmental refugees" has been discussed since the mid-1980s, when Essam El-Hinnawi offered the following definition: "People who have been forced to leave their traditional habitat, temporarily or permanently, because of a marked environmental disruption (natural and/or triggered by people) that jeopardized their existence and/or seriously affected the quality of their life."[14] El-Hinnawi has estimated that there are now perhaps 30 million environmental refugees.[15] A projection by environmental researcher Norman Myers that there could be as many as 250 million such refugees by mid-century has been widely cited but also has been criticized for some of its assumptions.[16]

No one is systematically collecting data on environmentally driven displacement—in part because there is no generally accepted definition and methodology. Some analysts argue that the category of refugees—legally defined as people fleeing persecution without access to protection by their own country—should not be muddied by other factors such as environmental degradation.[17] Others point to the fact that not everyone uprooted by environmental change crosses a border—and thus does not technically become a refugee, but rather an "environmentally displaced person."[18]

And there are now also increasing references to "climate refugees." Climate change will have serious human repercussions—in the form of

sea level rise, more frequent and more devastating weather events, freshwater shortages, disruption of agricultural systems, impaired ecosystem services, and health epidemics—that are bound to force people to relocate.[19]

Some people may be more aptly described as environmental migrants—moving, sometimes seasonally or temporarily, before the "push" of environmental degradation forces them to leave and with expectations of the "pull" of a better life elsewhere (or the prospect of being able to send money back home). As climate change takes center stage, however, it is likely that "push" will outweigh "pull."[20]

More than 600 million people live in low-lying coastal zones worldwide.[21] By some projections, at least 160 million people living in such areas may be at risk of flooding from storm surges by 2010.[22] Bangladesh, for instance, is already experiencing growing storm surges and rising salinity in coastal areas.[23] One third of the country could be flooded if the sea rises by one meter, affecting 20 million of its 140 million people.[24] In 2005, Hurricane Katrina caused 1.5 million people to be displaced temporarily; some 300,000 may never return to their former homes.[25] Meanwhile, small island states like the Maldives in the Indian Ocean and Tuvalu in the Pacific face the danger of being entirely devoured by sea level rise.[26] Low-lying, heavily populated deltas similarly face the specter of inundation.

Arid and semiarid areas cover about 40 percent of Earth's land surface and are home to more than 2 billion people.[27] Desertification processes put an estimated 135 million people worldwide at risk of being driven from their lands.[28] Where people—typically women—already have to walk many kilometers each day to fetch water, such as in the Sahel, longer journeys are simply not an option.[29] Water shortages could affect anywhere from 75 million to 250 million people in Africa by 2020 and more than 1 billion people in Asia by 2050.[30]

The precise nature of environmental change can make a big difference in terms of displacements. Fast-onset impacts like floods and storms will affect people in different ways than a gradual process like drought and desertification or sea level rise. The severity and frequency of disasters, too, has important impacts on the habitability and economic viability of affected areas.

Resilience is a key factor determining whether vulnerability translates into flight. The poor are typically most exposed to environmental hazards. Population pressures and social marginalization often compel them to live in risky places—steep hillsides likely to be hit by landslides, low-lying areas susceptible to flooding, or coastal strips whose natural buffers (wetlands, mangroves, and coral reefs) have been stripped away. And they often have limited capacity to deal with these challenges, sometimes even lacking the necessary monetary resources, family networks, or other connections needed to migrate.[31]

Adaptation measures can help reduce vulnerability: disaster and famine early warning systems, livelihood diversification, drought-resistant crops, restoration of ecosystems, flood-

defense infrastructure, crop insurance, and others. But even in the wake of floods or storms, well-calibrated emergency and recovery aid can make the difference between people staying and leaving. Resilience is also a function of overall economic capacity, demographic pressures, governance structures, and good leadership, as well as social and political cohesiveness.[32]

So far, international funding for adaptation in poorer and more vulnerable countries is woefully limited.[33] Yet timely adaptation—along with mitigation measures to prevent the worst of climate change—will be much less costly in economic and human terms than dealing with disasters and displacements. UNHCR already struggles to provide adequate support for refugees and internally displaced people, and the same is true for agencies providing humanitarian aid. They will be overwhelmed if the large-scale climate-related displacements now predicted indeed come to pass.

Notes

GRAIN HARVEST SETS RECORD, BUT SUPPLIES STILL TIGHT (pages 12–14)

1. U.N. Food and Agriculture Organization (FAO), *FAOSTAT Statistical Database*, at faostat.fao.org, updated 30 June 2007; FAO, *Crop Prospects and Food Situation, No. 5* (Rome: October 2007). Harvest in 2007 is an estimate. This figure includes rice measured as "paddy" rather than the smaller "milled" figure in order to correspond with international convention.
2. FAO, *Crop Prospects and Food Situation*, op. cit. note 1; U.S. Department of Agriculture (USDA), Foreign Agricultural Service (FAS), *Grain: World Markets and Trade*, October 2007 (Washington, DC: 2007).
3. FAO, *FAOSTAT*, op. cit. note 1.
4. Ibid.; U.S. Bureau of the Census, *International Data Base*, electronic database (Suitland, MD: updated 16 July 2007).
5. FAO, *FAOSTAT*, op. cit. note 1; Census Bureau, op. cit. note 4.
6. FAO, *FAOSTAT*, op. cit. note 1.
7. Ibid.
8. FAO, *Crop Prospects and Food Situation*, op. cit. note 1.
9. Ibid.
10. Ibid.
11. FAO, *FAOSTAT*, op. cit. note 1.
12. Fertilizer from Patrick Heffer and Michel Prud'homme, *Medium-Term Outlook for Global Fertilizer Demand, Supply and Trade 2007–2011: Summary Report,* presented at 75th International Fertilizer Association Annual Conference, Istanbul, Turkey, 21–23 May 2007.
13. FAO, *FAOSTAT*, op. cit. note 1.
14. Ibid.
15. Ibid.
16. FAO, *Crop Prospects and Food Situation*, op. cit. note 1.
17. Ibid.
18. Ibid.
19. Ibid.
20. Ibid.
21. Ibid.
22. USDA, FAS, *Grain: World Markets and Trade*, September 2007 (Washington, DC: 2007).
23. FAO, *Crop Prospects and Food Situation*, op. cit. note 1.
24. Ibid.
25. USDA, *Production, Supply & Distribution*, online database available at www.fas.usda.gov/psdonline, updated 20 November 2007.
26. Ibid.
27. FAO, *Crop Prospects and Food Situation*, op. cit. note 1; USDA, op. cit. note 2.
28. FAO, *Crop Prospects and Food Situation*, op. cit. note 1.
29. Ibid.
30. USDA, op. cit. note 22.
31. Ibid.
32. FAO, "Wheat Prices Hit Record-high Levels," press release (Rome: 5 October 2007).
33. FAO, *Crop Prospects and Food Situation*, op. cit. note 1.
34. Celia W. Dugger, "As Prices Soar, U.S. Food Aid Buys Less," *New York Times*, 29 September 2007.
35. Ibid.
36. FAO, *The State of Food Insecurity in the World 2006* (Rome: 2006).

MEAT PRODUCTION CONTINUES TO RISE (15–17)

1. U.N. Food and Agriculture Organization (FAO), "Meat and Meat Products," *Food Outlook*, June 2008.
2. FAO, *Livestock's Long Shadow, Environmental Issues*

and Options (Rome: 2007), p. xx.

3. Henning Steinfeld and Pius Chilonda, "Old Players, New Players," in FAO, *Livestock Report 2006* (Rome: 2006), p. 3.

4. FAO, op. cit. note 1.

5. Ibid.

6. Ibid.

7. Ibid.

8. Ibid.

9. Ibid.

10. Ibid.

11. Ibid.

12. Ibid.

13. Ibid.

14. Ibid.

15. Ibid.

16. FAO, op. cit. note 3; FAO, op. cit. note 2.

17. FAO, *FAOSTAT Statistical Database*, at faostat.fao.org, updated 30 June 2007.

18. FAO, Commission on Genetic Resources for Food and Agriculture, *The State of the World's Animal Genetic Resources for Food and Agriculture* (Rome: 2007).

19. FAO, *FAOSTAT Statistical Database*, at faostat.fao.org, updated 24 January 2006; Compassion in World Farming, Laying Hens Fact Sheet, revised January 2004, at www.ciwf.org.uk/publications/Factsheets/Factsheet%20-%20Laying%20Hens%20.pdf.

20. M. Pollan, "The Life of a Steer," *New York Times*, 31 March 2002.

21. World Bank, *Managing the Livestock Revolution: Policy and Technology to Address the Negative Impacts of a Fast-Growing Sector* (Washington, DC: 2005), p. 6.

22. Paul Brown et al., "Bovine Spongiform Encephalopathy and Variant Creutzfeldt-Jacob Disease: Background, Evolution, and Current Concerns," *Emerging Infectious Diseases*, January-February 2001, pp. 6–14; World Health Organization, "Bovine Spongiform Encephalopathy," fact sheet (Geneva: revised November 2002).

23. Margaret Mellon, Charles Benbrook, and Karen Lutz Benbrook, *Hogging It! Estimates of Antimicrobial Abuse in Livestock* (Washington, DC: Union of Concerned Scientists, 2001).

24. Ibid.

25. FAO, op. cit. note 2.

26. Ibid., p. xx.

27. Ibid.

28. Ibid.

29. FAO, *Pollution from Industrialized Livestock Production*, Policy Brief 2 (Rome: Livestock Information,

Sector Analysis, and Policy Branch, Animal Production and Health Division, undated).

30. Ibid.

31. L. Baroni et al., "Evaluating the Environmental Impact of Various Dietary Patterns Combined with Different Food Prodution Systems," *European Journal of Clinical Nutrition*, February 2007, pp. 279–86.

32. A. J. McMichael et al., "Food, Livestock Production, Energy, Climate Change, and Health," *The Lancet* (Energy and Health Series), 6 October 2007, pp. 1253–63.

GENETICALLY MODIFIED CROPS ONLY A FRACTION OF PRIMARY GLOBAL CROP PRODUCTION (pages 18–20)

1. Clive James, *Global Status of Commercialized Biotech/GM Crops: 2007*, Brief 37 (Ithaca, NY: International Service for the Acquisition of Agri-biotech Applications (ISAAA), 2007), p. 3. ISAAA is the only source tracking global GM crop area statistics; some critics have charged that its numbers are often inflated (see, for example, Friends of the Earth International (FOEI), *Who Benefits from GM Crops? The Rise in Pesticide Use* (Amsterdam: January 2008)).

2. Worldwatch calculations based on 2007 "primary crops" grouping per each country in ProdSTAT section of Food and Agriculture Organization (FAO), *FAOSTAT Statistical Database*, at faostat.fao.org, updated 11 June 2008, and on James, op. cit. note 1, p. 5.

3. James, op. cit. note 1, p. 10.

4. Ibid., pp. 3–4. Country income levels based on World Bank classifications as of 15 November 2008, at web.worldbank.org/WBSITE/EXTERNAL/DATASTATISTICS/0,,contentMDK:20421402~pagePK:64133150~piPK:64133175~theSitePK:239419,00.html#Low_income.

5. Clive James and A. F. Krattiger, *Global Review of the Field Testing and Commercialization of Transgenic Plants, 1986 to 1995: The First Decade of Crop Biotechnology*, Brief 1 (Ithaca, NY: ISAAA, 1996), p. 23; James, op. cit. note 1, p. 5.

6. James, op. cit. note 1, p. 5; Clive James, *Global Status of Commercialized Biotech/GM Crops: 2006*, Brief 35 (Ithaca, NY: ISAAA, 2006), p. 6.

7. Sean Hao, "Papaya Production Taking a Tumble," *Alaska Advertiser*, 19 March 2006; Jim Christie, "Ban on Monsanto Genetically Modified Alfalfa Upheld," *Reuters*, 3 May 2007; U.S. Federal Register, Animal

and Plant Health Inspection Service, "Notice: Environmental Impact Statement; Determination of Regulated Status of Alfalfa Genetically Engineered for Tolerance to the Herbicide Glyphosate," Docket No. APHIS-2007-0044, 7 January 2008, pp. 1198–1200.

8. James, op. cit. note 1, p. 5.

9. Ibid.

10. Ibid.

11. Ibid.

12. James and Krattiger, op. cit. note 5, p. 23; James, op. cit. note 1, p. 5; James, op. cit. note 6, p. 6; Clive James, *Global Status of Commercialized Transgenic Crops: 2005*, Brief 34 (Ithaca, NY: ISAAA, 2005), p. 9; Clive James, *Preview: Global Status of Commercialized Transgenic Crops: 2004*, Brief 32 (Ithaca, NY: ISAAA, 2004), p. 11; Clive James, *Preview: Global Status of Commercialized Transgenic Crops: 2003*, Brief 30 (Ithaca, NY: ISAAA, 2003), p. 9.

13. James, op. cit. note 1, p. 5; James, op. cit. note 6, p. 6.

14. James, op. cit. note 1, p. 7.

15. Ibid., p. 11.

16. Jorge Fernandez-Cornejo and William D. McBride, with contributions from Hisham El-Osta et al., "Adoption of Bioengineered Crops," *Agricultural Economic Report*, No. 810 (Washington, DC: Economic Research Service (ERS), U.S. Department of Agriculture (USDA), 2002), p. 4.

17. James, op. cit. note 1, p. 11.

18. Ibid.; James, op. cit. note 6, p. 5; James, *Global Status 2005*, op. cit. note 12, pp. 34–35; James, *Global Status 2004*, op. cit. note 12, pp. 20–21; James, *Global Status 2003*, op. cit. note 12, pp. 17–18; Clive James, *Preview: Global Status of Commercialized Transgenic Crops: 2002*, Brief 26 (Ithaca, NY: ISAAA, 2002), p. 12; Clive James, *Global Review of Commercialized Transgenic Crops: 2001*, Brief 24 (Ithaca, NY: ISAAA, 2001), pp. 11–12; Clive James, *Global Status of Commercialized Transgenic Crops: 2000*, Brief 23 (Ithaca, NY: ISAAA, 2001), p. 10.

19. Charles Benbrook, "Genetically Engineered Crops and Pesticide Use in the United States: The First Nine Years," *BioTech InfoNet*, Technical Paper Number 7, October 2004; FOEI, op. cit. note 1; Fernandez-Cornejo and McBride, op. cit. note 16.

20. Chris Boerboom and Michael Owen, "Facts about Glyphosate-Resistant Weeds," The Glyphosate Weed and Crop Series, Glyphosate Stewardship Working Group, December 2006; Ian Heap, Weed Science, *Glycines (G/9) Resistant Weeds By Species and Country*, online database, at www.weedscience.org/Summary/ UspeciesMOA.asp?lstMOAID=12&FmHRACGroup= Go, viewed 18 November 2008.

21. Boerboom and Owen, op. cit. note 20; Bob Hartzler, "Glyphosate Resistance in the Cornbelt," Iowa State University Weed Science Web site, at www.weeds .iastate.edu/mgmt/2005/pennpaper.shtml, viewed 27 October 2008.

22. James, op. cit. note 1, p. 11; Jorge Fernandez-Cornejo and Margriet Caswell, *The First Decade of Genetically Engineered Crops in the United States*, Economic Information Bulletin Number 11 (Washington, DC: ERS, USDA, 2006), p. 9; Roger W. Elmore et al., "Glyphosate-Resistant Soybean Cultivar Yields Compared with Sister Lines," *Agronomy Journal*, March-April 2001, pp. 408–12.

23. Elmore et al., op. cit. note 22; International Assessment of Agricultural Knowledge, Science and Technology for Development (IAASTD), *Executive Summary of the Synthesis Report* (Washington, DC: April 2008).

24. Chad Heeter, "Seeds of Suicide: India's Desperate Farmers," *Frontline/World: Rough Cut*, 26 July 2005.

25. James, op. cit. note 1, p. 12; Clive James, *Global Review of Commercialized Transgenic Crops: 1998*, Brief 8 (Ithaca, NY: ISAAA, 2001), pp. 34–37.

26. World Health Organization (WHO), *Modern Food Biotechnology, Human Health, and Development: An Evidence-Based Study* (Geneva: Food Safety Department, 2005), pp. 12–17; Philip J. Dale, Belinda Clarke, and Eliana M.G. Fontes, "Potential for the Environmental Impact of Transgenic Crops," *Nature Biotechnology*, June 2002, pp. 567–74; FAO, *Report of the Panel of Eminent Experts on Ethics in Food and Agriculture*, First Session (Rome: 2001); IAASTD, op. cit. note 23, p. 14.

27. FAO, *Potential Impacts of Genetic Use Restriction Technologies (GURTs) on Agricultural Biodiversity and Agricultural Production Systems: Technical Study* (Rome: 2002); Sergio H. Lence and Dermot J. Hayes, "Technology Fees versus GURTs in the Presence of Spillovers: World Welfare Impacts," *AgBioForum*, vol. 8, nos. 2 & 3 (2005), pp. 172–86.

28. FAO, op. cit. note 27; "Terminator Gene Halt a 'Major U-Turn,'" *BBC News*, 5 October 1999; Transcontainer, "Transcontainer & Controllable Fertility," fact sheet (Netherlands: undated).

29. World Bank, *World Development Report 2008* (Washington, DC: 2007), pp. 15, 177–78; FAO, "FAO Warns of 'Molecular Divide' between North and South; Biotechnology: The Gap between Poor and Rich Countries Is Widening," press release (Rome:

18 February 2003).

30. World Bank, op. cit. note 29, pp. 15, 177–78; WHO, op. cit. note 26, pp. 53–55; FAO, *The State of Food and Agriculture: Agricultural Biotechnology, Meeting the Needs of the Poor?* (Rome: 2004), pp. 25–39, 87–93.

31. FAO, op. cit. note 29; FAO, op. cit. note 30.

32. IAASTD, op. cit. note 23.

33. FAO, op. cit. note 30, pp. 25–39.

34. Worldwatch calculations based on Monsanto, "Biotechnology Trait Acreage: Fiscal Years 1996–2008F," information sheet (St. Louis, MO: 25 June 2008), and on James, op. cit. note 1, p. 3; percent of seed market from ETC Group, *Who Owns Nature? Corporate Power and the Final Frontier in the Commodification of Life* (Ottawa, Canada: November 2008), p. 11.

35. Center for Food Safety, *Monsanto vs. U.S. Farmers: November 2007 Update* (Washington, DC: 2007).

36. Ibid.; Bernard Simon, "Monsanto Wins Patent Case on Plant Genes," *New York Times*, 22 May 2004; Donald L. Barlett and James B. Steele, "Monsanto's Harvest of Fear," *Vanity Fair*, May 2008.

37. Sarah Gardner, "Monsanto Makes the Case for GM Crops," *Marketplace*, 4 June 2008.

38. Andrew Pollack, "In Lean Times, Biotech Grains Are Less Taboo," *New York Times*, 21 April 2008.

39. IAASTD, op. cit. note 23.

40. James, op. cit. note 1, p. 12.

41. U.S. Environmental Protection Agency, *Greenhouse Gas Impacts of Expanded Renewable and Alternative Fuels Use* (Washington, DC: 2007).

42. Carey Gillam, "Biotech Companies Race for Drought-Tolerant Crops," *Reuters*, 14 January 2008; ETC Group, *Patenting the "Climate Genes"…And Capturing the Climate Agenda* (Ottawa, Canada: May/June 2008).

43. African Agricultural Technology Foundation, "African Agricultural Technology Foundation to Develop Drought-Tolerant Maize Varieties for Small-Scale Farmers in Africa," press release (Kampala, Uganda: 19 March 2008).

44. Gio Braidotti, "Scientists Share Keys to Drought Tolerance," *Ground Cover Issue 72* (Barton, Australia: Australian Government Grains Research and Development Corporation, January-February 2008).

45. James, op. cit. note 1, p. 13.

46. Council of the European Union, "2898th Council Meeting: Environment (in Luxembourg)," press release (Brussels: 20 October 2008); Geoffrey Lean, "Safety Fears Prompt Europe to Consider First Ban on GM Crop," (London) *The Independent*, 25 November 2007; Geoffrey Lean, "Europe's Secret Plan to Boost GM Crop Production: Gordon Brown and Other EU Leaders in Campaign to Promote Modified Foods," (London) *The Independent*, 26 October 2008.

47. "France Halts Genetically Modified Corn," *Associated Press*, 9 February 2008; James, op. cit. note 1, p. 13.

48. James, op. cit. note 1, p. 12; World Bank, op. cit. note 29, p. 177.

49. Alberta Velimirov, Claudia Binter, and Jürgen Zentek, *Biological Effects of Transgenic Maize NK603xMON810 Fed in Long Term Reproduction Studies in Mice* (Vienna: Austrian Ministry of Health, Families, and Youth, 2008).

50. Jeff Randall, "Prince Charles Warns GM Crops Risk Causing the Biggest-Ever Environmental Disaster," (London) *The Telegraph*, 12 August 2008.

FISH FARMING CONTINUES TO GROW AS WORLD FISHERIES STAGNATE (pages 21–23)

1. U.N. Food and Agriculture Organization (FAO), FISHSTAT electronic database, at www.fao.org/fishery/statistics/software/fishstat, updated March 2008.

2. Ibid.

3. Ibid.

4. FAO, *The State of World Fisheries and Aquaculture 2006* (Rome: 2006), p. 3. Calculation from Table 1.

5. Ibid., pp. 3–5.

6. Ibid., p. 3.

7. Ibid., pp. 36–37.

8. Ibid.

9. Ibid., pp. 37–38.

10. National Marine Fisheries Service, *Fisheries of the United States 2007* (Silver Spring, MD: 2008), pp. 73–77.

11. FAO, op. cit. note 1; FAO, "Meat and Meat Products," *Food Outlook*, June 2008; FAO, *FAOSTAT Statistical Database*, at faostat.fao.org, updated 24 January 2006.

12. Ibid.

13. FAO, op. cit. note 4, p. 41.

14. Ibid., p. 7.

15. Ibid., pp. 7, 151.

16. Ibid., pp. 10, 29.

17. Ibid., p. 16.

18. Ibid.; FAO, op. cit. note 1.

19. FAO, op. cit. note 1.

20. Ibid.
21. World Bank, *Changing the Face of the Waters: The Promise and Challenge of Sustainable Aquaculture* (Washington, DC: 2007), p. 18.
22. Ibid., p. 68.
23. FAO, op. cit. note 1.
24. Ibid.
25. Brooke Campbell and Jackie Alder, "Fishmeal and Fish Oil: Production, Trade and Consumption," in Jackie Alder and David Pauly, eds., *On the Multiple Uses of Forage Fish: From Ecosystems to Markets*, Fisheries Centre Research Reports (Vancouver, Canada: Fisheries Centre, University of British Columbia, 2006), pp. 48, 59–61.
26. Reg Watson, Jackie Alder, and Daniel Pauly, "Fisheries for Forage Fish, 1950 to the Present," in Alder and Pauly, op. cit. note 25, p. 3.
27. Campbell and Alder, op. cit. note 25, pp. 60–62.
28. Ibid., p. 62.
29. Dirk Zeller et al., "Global Dispersion of Dioxin: A Spatial Dynamic Model, With Emphasis on Ocean Deposition," in Alder and Pauly, op. cit. note 25, p. 68.
30. U.S. Environmental Protection Agency, "Frequent Questions About Mercury," at publicaccess.custhelp .com/cgi-bin/publicaccess.cfg/php/enduser/std_alp .php?p_lva=&p_li=&p_accessibility=0&p_redirect= &p_page=1&p_cv=&p_pv=1.233&p_prods=233& p_cats=&p_hidden_prods=&prod_lvl1=233&p_sea rch_text=&p_new_search=1, updated 5 December 2008.
31. Peter Tyedmers et al., *Biophysical Sustainability and Approaches to Marine Aquaculture Development Policy in the United States*, report to the Marine Aquaculture Task Force (Takoma Park, MD: Marine Aquaculture Task Force, February 2007), p. 21.
32. Ibid., p. 20.
33. Barry A. Costa-Pierce, "Ecology as the Paradigm for the Future of Aquaculture," in Barry Costa-Pierce, ed., *Ecological Aquaculture: The Evolution of the Blue Revolution* (Oxford, U.K.: Blackwell, 2003), pp. 339–72.
34. Malcolm MacGarvin, *Scotland's Secret? Aquaculture, Nutrient Pollution, Eutrophication, and Toxic Blooms*, report prepared by Modus Vivendi (Perth, Scotland: WWF Scotland, 2000); Rosamond Naylor and Marshall Burke, "Aquaculture and Ocean Resources: Raising Tigers of the Sea," *Annual Review of Environmental Resources*, vol. 30 (2005), pp. 185–218.
35. Ibid.
36. See, for example, Brian Halweil, *Farming Fish for the Future*, Worldwatch Report 176 (Washington, DC:

Worldwatch Institute, 2008).
37. World Bank, op. cit. note 21, p. 33.
38. FAO, op. cit. note 4, p. 36.
39. World Bank, op. cit. note 21.
40. World Bank, *Turning the Tide, Saving Fish and Fishers: Building Sustainable and Equitable Fisheries and Governance* (Washington, DC: 2005), p. 4.

COAL USE RISES DRAMATICALLY DESPITE IMPACTS ON CLIMATE AND HEALTH (pages 26–28)

1. Worldwatch calculation based on: fossil fuel, nuclear, and hydroelectric energy consumption reported in BP, *Statistical Review of World Energy* (London: 2007), and renewable energy consumption from International Energy Agency (IEA), *Key World Energy Statistics* (Paris: 2007), from REN21, *Renewables Global Status Report 2007* (Paris and Washington, DC: REN21 Secretariat and Worldwatch Institute, 2008), and from Christoph Berg, senior analyst, F.O. Licht, e-mails to Rodrigo G. Pinto, Worldwatch Institute, 20–22 March 2007.
2. Christopher Flavin, "Building a Low-Carbon Economy," in Worldwatch Institute, *State of the World 2008* (New York: W. W. Norton & Company, 2008); BP, op. cit. note 1.
3. BP, op. cit. note 1.
4. Worldwatch calculation based on BP, op. cit. note 1.
5. Ibid.
6. U.S. Department of Energy (DOE), Energy Information Administration (EIA), "Generating Unit Additions in the United States by State, Company and Plant, 2006," Excel workbook, 2 February 2007; Government of India, Ministry of Power, Central Electricity Authority, "Monthly Review of Power Sector (Executive Summary)," 31 January 2006 and 31 January 2007.
7. China Electricity Council, "2006 Statistics Report for the National Power Industry," press release (Beijing: 12 January 2007).
8. Massachusetts Institute of Technology (MIT), *The Future of Coal; Options for a Carbon-Constrained World* (Cambridge, MA: 2007), p. 64; Hajime Akimoto et al., "Verification of Energy Consumption in China during 1996–2003 by Using Satellite Observational Data," *Atmospheric Environment*, vol. 40 (2006), pp. 7663–67; Jonathan Sinton, "Accuracy and Reliability of China's Energy Statistics," *China Economic Review*, vol. 12 (2001), pp. 373–83.
9. Richard McGregor, "China's Power Capacity Soars,"

Financial Times, 6 February 2007.

10. U.S. Department of Labor, Mine Safety and Health Administration, *2006 Fatalgrams and Fatal Investigation Reports* (Washington, DC: December 2006); "China Sees Coal Mine Deaths Fall, But Outlook Grim," *Reuters*, 10 January 2007.

11. Richard McGregor, "750,000 a Year Killed by Chinese Pollution," *Financial Times*, 2 July 2007.

12. Peter Fairley, "Part II: China's Coal Future," *Technology Review*, 5 January 2007.

13. U.S. Department of Justice, "U.S. Announces Largest Single Environmental Settlement in History," press release (Washington, DC: October 2007).

14. DOE, EIA, "Form EIA-860 Database, Annual Electric Generator Report," Excel workbook, 2005 version.

15. DOE, EIA, *Annual Coal Report 2005* (Washington, DC: October 2006), p. 33; Geological Survey of India, *Indian Coal Resources as on 01-04-2007* (Kolkata: January 2007).

16. Zaipu Tao and Mingyu Li, "What Is the Limit of Chinese Coal Supplies—A STELLA Model of Hubbert Peak," *Energy Policy*, vol. 35 (2007), pp. 3145–54; World Energy Council, *2007 Survey of Energy Resources* (London: 2007), p. 26.

17. ACT MAP Scenario from IEA, *Energy Technology Perspectives—Scenarios & Strategies to 2050* (Paris: 2006), p. 65; business-as-usual scenario from MIT, op. cit. note 8, p. 11.

18. MIT, op. cit. note 8, p. 7.

19. Nicholas Stern, "What Does the Stern Review Mean for the UN Climate Change Meeting in Bali?" presentation at Environmental and Energy Study Institute, Washington, DC, 21 September 2007.

20. MIT, op. cit. note 8; Nicholas Stern, *The Economics of Climate Change: The Stern Review* (Cambridge, U.K.: Cambridge University Press, 2007); Intergovernmental Panel on Climate Change, *Carbon Dioxide Capture and Storage* (Geneva: 2005).

21. Electric Power Research Institute (EPRI), "CO_2 Capture and Storage," *EPRI Journal*, spring 2007, p. 9.

22. Ibid.; Peter Fairley, "Carbon Dioxide for Sale," *Technology Review*, July 2005; IEA, *IEA GHG Weyburn CO_2 Monitoring & Storage Project* (Cheltenham: undated), p. 19.

23. Carbon dioxide emissions from enhanced oil production at the Weyburn oil field calculated by Worldwatch based on production estimates from IEA, op. cit. note 22, and approximate crude oil carbon content from DOE, *Emissions of Greenhouse Gases in the United States 1998* (Washington, DC: November 1999), Table B4.

24. MIT, op. cit. note 8, pp. 19, 30.

25. EPRI, op. cit. note 21, p. 16; MIT, op. cit. note 8, p. 145.

26. DOE, National Energy Technology Laboratory, *Carbon Sequestration Technology Roadmap and Program Plan* (Washington, DC: 2007); MIT, op. cit. note 8, p. 48.

27. DOE, op. cit. note 26, p. 10; MIT, op. cit. note 8, pp. xii, 52.

28. Total, "A Pilot Installation at Lacq. Carbon Dioxide Capture and Storage," at www.total.com, viewed 27 September 2007; EPRI, op. cit. note 21; Vattenfall, *Vattenfall's CO_2-Free Power Plant Project* at vattenfall.com, viewed 26 November 2007; American Electric Power, "AEP to Install Carbon Capture on Two Existing Power Plants; Company Will be First to Move Technology to Commercial Scale," press release (Columbus, OH: 15 March 2007).

29. European Commission, Directorate-General for Energy and Transport, *Energy for a Changing World* (Brussels: 2007).

30. Office of Senator Harry Reid, "Reid: Decline of Coal Power Plant Construction Nationally Should Be a Message to Nevada," press release (Washington, DC: 14 September 2007); California Public Utilities Commission, "PUC Sets GHG Emissions Performance Standard to Help Mitigate Climate Change," press release (San Francisco: 25 January 2007).

31. Citigroup, *Coal: Missing the Window* (18 July 2007).

32. Government of India, Planning Commission, *Integrated Energy Policy: Report of the Expert Committee* (New Delhi: 2006); MIT, op. cit. note 8, p. 63; IEA, *World Energy Outlook, 2006* (Paris: 2006).

OIL CONSUMPTION CONTINUES SLOW GROWTH (pages 29–31)

1. Worldwatch calculation based on global petroleum consumption data from U.S. Energy Information Administration (EIA), *Short-Term Energy Outlook (STEO) – March 2008*, Report and Excel Workbook (Washington, DC: 2008), from BP, *Statistical Review of World Energy*, Excel Workbook (London: 2007), and from EIA, *February 2008 Monthly Energy Review (MER)* (Washington, DC: February 2008).

2. EIA, *STEO*, op. cit. note 1.

3. Worldwatch calculation based on EIA, "Daily Spot

Prices for Crude Oil and Petroleum Products," Excel Workbook, 11 March 2008.

4. EIA, *STEO*, op. cit. note 1.

5. Ibid.; U.S. Federal Reserve, "Real Gross Domestic Product—Percent Change from Year Ago," Excel Workbook, February 2008; *BBCNews.com*, "US Economic Growth Drops Sharply," *BBCNews.com* (online international version), 30 January 2008.

6. Worldwatch calculation based on EIA, *STEO*, op. cit. note 1, and on EIA, *MER*, op. cit. note 1.

7. Ibid.

8. Ibid.; BP, op. cit. note 1.

9. Worldwatch calculation based on EIA, *STEO*, op. cit. note 1, and on EIA, *MER*, op. cit. note 1; BP, op. cit. note 1.

10. EIA, op. cit. note 3; Worldwatch calculation also based on U.S. Federal Reserve, "Spot Oil Price: West Texas Intermediate," Excel Workbook, January 2007.

11. EIA, op. cit. note 3; Jad Mouawad, "Oil Prices Pass Record Set in '80s, but Then Recede," *New York Times*, 3 March 2008.

12. EIA, *STEO*, op. cit. note 1, p. 1.

13. International Energy Agency, *Oil Market Report—January 2008* (Paris: 2008); Russell Gold and Ann Davis, "Oil Officials See Limit Looming on Production," *Wall Street Journal*, 17 November 2007.

14. EIA, *MER* , op. cit. note 1, Table 11.1.

15. Ibid.

16. Ibid.

17. Jad Mouawad, "As Economy Lags in U.S., Oil Nations Rethink Cuts," *New York Times*, 3 March 2008; "Saudis Said to Plan Production Cuts," *CNN.com*, 30 January 2007.

18. Worldwatch calculation based on EIA, *MER*, op. cit. note 1, Table 11.1.

19. EIA, *MER*, op. cit. note 1; EIA, *STEO*, op. cit. note 1; BP, op. cit. note 1.

20. Worldwatch calculation based on EIA, *STEO*, op. cit. note 1; Guy Chazan, "Russia Oil Output to Rise Modestly," *Wall Street Journal*, 16 November 2007.

21. Keith Johnson, "For Peak Oil, Three's a Crowd," *Environmental Capital, Wall Street Journal* blog, 25 January 2008.

22. Steve Hargreaves, "The End of Oil," *CNN.com*, 14 September 2007.

23. CBS/AP, "Iraq Primed for Oil Windfall, U.S. Says," *CBSNews.com*, 30 January 2008.

24. Worldwatch calculation based on EIA, *STEO*, op. cit. note 1.

25. Tume Ahemba, "Nigeria Rebel Group Declares Christmas Ceasefire," *Alertnet.org* (Reuters), 22 December 2007; Fidelis Mbah, "Nigeria Oil City in Slum Clean-up," *BBCNews.com*, 27 August 2007.

26. Ahemba, op. cit. note 25; Worldwatch calculation based on EIA, *STEO*, op. cit. note 1.

27. Guy Chazan, "Bombings and Threats Shake Algeria Outlook," *Wall Street Journal*, 14 December 2007.

28. Chevron in Russell Gold, "Exxon Posts Record Profit," *Wall Street Journal*, 4 February 2008; Guy Chazan, "Shell Warns on Output After Profit Gusher," *Wall Street Journal*, 1 February 2008.

29. Russell Gold, "Exxon Posts Biggest Profit in U.S. History," *Wall Street Journal*, 2 February 2008.

30. Steve Goldstein, "Exxon Struggling to Replace Reserves, Analyst Says," *Marketwatch.com*, 18 February 2008; Cyrus Sanati and Antony Currie, "Is Exxon Mobil Going Dry?" *Wall Street Journal*, 20 February 2008; Jeffrey Ball and Russell Gold, "Exxon Has Off Year Discovering New Oil," *Wall Street Journal*, 16 February 2008.

31. BP, op. cit. note 1.

WIND POWER CONTINUES RAPID RISE (pages 32–34)

1. Global Wind Energy Council (GWEC), "US, China & Spain Lead World Wind Power Market in 2007," press release (Brussels: 15 February 2008); GWEC, "Global Wind Installations Pass 100 GW, and Are Predicted to Rise to 240 GW by 2012," press release (Brussels: 1 April 2008). Figure 1 from the following: BTM Consult, European Wind Energy Association (EWEA), American Wind Energy Association (AWEA), *Windpower Monthly*, *New Energy*; 2005 data are a Worldwatch estimate based on GWEC, "Global Wind Energy Markets Continue to Boom—2006 Another Record Year," press release (Brussels: 2 February 2007); 2006 and 2007 data from GWEC, Table: "Global Installed Wind Power Capacity (MW)–Regional Distribution," 2008, at www.gwec .net, viewed 4 April 2008.

2. GWEC, "US, China & Spain Lead," op. cit. note 1. Figure 2 from sources for Figure 1 cited in note 1.

3. EWEA, "Wind Energy Leads EU Power Installations in 2007, But National Growth is Inconsistent," press release (Brussels: 4 February 2008).

4. AWEA, "Wind Power Outlook 2008," at www.awea .org/Market_Report_Jan08.pdf. Figure 3 from the following: 1980–2001 for Germany from Bundesverband WindEnergie (BWE), EWEA; United States from Paul Gipe, AWEA; Spain from Instituto para

Diversificacion y Ahorro Energetico; 2002–04 from BTM Consult ApS, EWEA, AWEA; 2005 from GWEC, "Record Year for Wind Energy: Global Wind Power Market Increased by 43% in 2005," press release (Brussels: 17 February 2006); 2006 from GWEC, "Global Wind Energy Markets Continue to Boom," op. cit. note 1; 2007 from GWEC, "Global Installed Wind Power Capacity," op. cit. note 1; China data from Shi Pengfei, "Wind Power in China," presentation, Guangzhou, China, 23 March 2007, and from Shi Pengfei, "2006 Wind Installa-tions in China" (Beijing, China General Certification Center, 2007), both cited in Eric Martinot and Jun-feng Li, *Powering China's Development: The Role of Renewable Energy*, Special Report (Washington, DC: Worldwatch Institute, November 2007), and from GWEC, "Global Installed Wind Power Capacity," op. cit. note 1.

5. AWEA, op. cit. note 4.

6. AWEA, "Installed U.S. Wind Power Capacity Surged 45% in 2007: American Wind Energy Association Market Report," press release (Washington: 17 Janu-ary 2008).

7. States from REN21, *Renewables 2007 Global Status Report* (Paris and Washington, DC: REN21 Secre-tariat and Worldwatch Institute, 2008), p. 25.

8. Texas and 30 percent from Graham Jesmer, "Wind Power Helps Texas Move Past Oil," RenewableEner-gyAccess.com, 28 November 2008; six states from AWEA, op. cit. note 4.

9. EWEA, op. cit. note 3.

10. Ibid.

11. Ibid.

12. Nearly 4 percent from ibid.; carbon dioxide avoided from GWEC, "US, China & Spain Lead," op. cit. note 1.

13. European share from GWEC, "US, China & Spain Lead," op. cit. note 1; 60 percent is Worldwatch cal-culation based on ibid. and on EWEA, op. cit. note 3.

14. Germany total from EWEA, "Wind Power Installed in Europe by End of 2007 (cumulative)," map and tables, at www.ewea.org, viewed 13 February 2008; share of global total is Worldwatch calculation based on ibid. and on GWEC, "US, China & Spain Lead," op. cit. note 1.

15. Andreas Wagner, GE Wind Energy, Salzbergen, Ger-many, discussion with author, 28 March 2008.

16. Installations in 2007 from EWEA, op. cit. note 14; 25 percent less from "World Wind Energy Market to Grow in '08—German VDMA," *Reuters*, 23 January 2008.

17. Share of electricity from renewables (6.3 percent) in 2000 from Jane Burgermeister, "EU to Fall Short of 2010 Renewable Energy Target," RenewableEnergy-World.com, 31 August 2007; share exceeded 14 percent by the end of 2007, from Erik Kirschbaum, "Europe's Renewables Lead Stirs US Concern—Germany," *Reuters*, 19 March 2008.

18. "Wind Wire," *Windpower Monthly*, February 2008, p. 8.

19. Ibid.

20. Total capacity from EWEA, op. cit. note 14; share of electricity needs from EWEA, op. cit. note 3.

21. EWEA, op. cit. note 14.

22. EWEA, op. cit. note 3.

23. Figure of 78 percent is Worldwatch calculation based on GWEC, "US, China & Spain Lead," op. cit. note 1, on AWEA, op. cit. note 6, and on EWEA, op. cit. note 3; more than 70 nations from GWEC, "Wind: A Global Power Source," at www.gwec.net, viewed 13 February 2008; Zimbabwe from Henry David Venema and Moussa Cisse, *Seeing the Light: Adapting to Climate Change with Decentralized Renew-able Energy in Developing Countries* (Winnipeg, MN, Canada: International Institute for Sustainable Development, 2004), p. 109.

24. GWEC, "US, China & Spain Lead," op. cit. note 1.

25. Additions in 2007 from ibid. and from Steve Sawyer, GWEC, discussion with author, 5 March 2008; total from GWEC, "US, China & Spain Lead," op. cit. note 1; target of 5,000 MW by 2010 from Martinot and Li, op. cit. note 4, p. 17.

26. "China Wind Power Hits 5.6 GW," RenewableEner gyWorld.com, 18 January 2008;" Sawyer, op. cit. note 25.

27. Prediction for 2008 from "China Wind Power Hits 5.6 GW," op. cit. note 26; 2015 prediction from GWEC, "US, China & Spain Lead," op. cit. note 1.

28. GWEC, "Top 10 Total Installed Capacity," and "Top 10 New Capacity," tables, at www.gwec.net, viewed 4 April 2008.

29. Canada, Brazil, Chile, and Egypt from Birger Mad-sen, BTM Consult ApS, e-mail to author, 20 Febru-ary 2008; New Zealand from GWEC, "Global Installed Wind Power Capacity," op. cit. note 1.

30. Keith Johnson, "Alternative Energy Hurt by a Wind-mill Shortage: While Projects in the U.S. Stall, Europe's Utilities Expand Their Reach," *Wall Street Journal*, 9 July 2007.

31. Ibid.

32. Ibid.
33. Stephen Lacey, "Despite Rising Costs, Wind Industry Thriving Worldwide," RenewableEnergyAccess.com, 26 July 2007.
34. Johnson, op. cit. note 30.
35. GWEC, op. cit. note 23.
36. Turbine shortage and materials costs from AWEA, op. cit. note 4; manufacturing profitability from Daniel Kammen, "A Snapshot of the U.S. Wind Industry," GreenBiz.com, December 2007.
37. Natural gas plants from Kammen, op. cit. note 36; all conventional plants from AWEA, op. cit. note 4.
38. GWEC, op. cit. note 23; REN21, op. cit. note 7, p. 16.
39. GWEC, op. cit. note 23.
40. Lyn Harrison, "A Momentous Proposal," *Windpower Monthly*, February 2008, p. 6.
41. Ibid.
42. BTM Consult ApS, *World Market Update 2002* (Ringköbing, Denmark: 2002), p. ix.

DESPITE OBSTACLES, BIOFUELS CONTINUE SURGE (pages 35–37)

1. Total world fuel ethanol and biodiesel production figures taken from REN21, *Renewables 2007 Global Status Report* (Paris and Washington, DC: REN21 Secretariat and Worldwatch Institute), Table R6 and p. 8, and from Rodrigo G. Pinto and Suzanne C. Hunt, "Biofuel Flows Surge," in Worldwatch Institute, *Vital Signs 2007–2008* (New York: W. W. Norton & Company, 2007), pp. 40–41, citing F.O. Licht.
2. Worldwatch calculation based on REN21, op. cit. note 1, and on Pinto and Hunt, op. cit. note 1.
3. Ibid.
4. Ibid.
5. Ibid; Christoph Berg, senior analyst, F.O. Licht, e-mails to Rodrigo G. Pinto, Worldwatch Institute, 20–22 March 2007.
6. Worldwatch calculation based on REN 21, op. cit. note 1, and on Renewable Fuels Association, *Changing the Climate: Ethanol Industry Outlook 2008* (Washington, DC: February 2008); Renewable Fuels Association, "Annual World Ethanol Production by Country," at www.ethanolrfa.org/industry/statistics/#E.
7. REN21, op. cit. note 1; Renewable Fuels Association, *Outlook 2008*, op. cit. note 6.
8. Renewable Fuels Association, *Outlook 2008*, op. cit. note 6, p. 2.
9. Ibid., p. 16.
10. REN21, op. cit. note 1, p. 13.
11. Worldwatch calculation from European Biodiesel Board, "2007 Production Capacity Statistics," at www.ebb-eu.org/stats.php.
12. Michael Hogan, "German Biodiesel Output Collapses," *Reuters.com*, 15 January 2008.
13. Ibid.; "German Biodiesel Firm Cuts Output as Sales Fall," *Reuters.com*, 26 March 2008.
14. "German Biodiesel Firm," op. cit. note 13.
15. European Biodiesel Board, op. cit. note 11.
16. REN21, op. cit. note 1, p. 15.
17. Renewable Fuels Association, *Outlook 2008*, op. cit. note 6, p. 8; Soo Ai Peng, "Record Oil Price Boosts Demand for Biofuels but Critics Question the Cost," *Forbes.com*, 19 October 2007.
18. Renewable Fuels Association, *Outlook 2008*, op. cit. note 6; Renewable Fuels Association, "Renewable Fuel Standard," at www.ethanolrfa.org/resource/standard.
19. REN21, op. cit. note 1, p. 28.
20. Ibid.; Masami Kojima, Donald Mitchell, and William Ward, *Considering Trade Policies for Liquid Biofuels*, World Bank Energy Sector Management and Assistance Program (Washington DC: April 2007), p. 47.
21. REN21, op. cit. note 1, p. 27.
22. Ibid., p. 16.
23. Ibid.
24. "New Energy Finance: New Clean Energy Investments in 2007 Totaled $117.2 Billion," *Clean Edge News*, 8 January 2008.
25. Ibid.
26. "Analyzing the Bull Run by Clean Energy Shares in 2007," New Energy Finance, press release (London: 16 January 2008).
27. "New Energy Finance," op. cit. note 24.
28. John Vidal, "Global Food Crisis Looms as Climate Change and Fuel Shortages Bite," (London) *The Guardian*, 3 November 2007.
29. Ibid.; Eli Clifton, "Biofuels Pushing Up Food Aid Prices," *Ipsnews.net*, 27 July 2007; Kathleen Kingsbury, "After the Oil Crisis, A Food Crisis?" *Time*, 16 November 2007.
30. Valerie Mercer-Blackman, Hossein Samiei, and Kevin Change, "Biofuel Demand Pushes Up Food Prices," *IMF Survey Magazine*, posted 17 October 2007; "Indian Minister Attacks Biofuels," *BBC News*, 26 March 2008.
31. Joseph Fargione et al., "Land Clearing and the Biofuel Carbon Debt," *Science*, 29 February 2008, pp.

1235–38; Timothy Searchinger et al., "Use of U.S. Croplands for Biofuels Increases Greenhouse Gases Through Emissions from Land Use Change," *Science*, 7 February 2008.

32. Elisabeth Rosenthal, "Once a Dream Fuel, Palm Oil May Be an Eco-Nightmare," *New York Times*, 31 January 2007.

33. Intergovernmental Panel on Climate Change, *Climate Change 2007: The Physical Science Basis* (New York: Cambridge University Press, 2007), p. 115; "UN Climate Change Conference," December 2007, at www.un.org/climatechange/blog/index.asp.

34. "Europe and US Take Clean Energy Lead While Japan Wavers," *New Energy Finance Week in Review*, 1–7 April 2008.

35. California Energy Commission "Low-Carbon Fuel Standard," at www.energy.ca.gov/low_carbon_fuel _standard.

36. Roundtable on Sustainable Palm Oil, at www.rspo.org.

37. Joel Bourne, Jr., "Green Dreams," *National Geographic*, October 2007, pp. 38–60.

ANOTHER SUNNY YEAR FOR SOLAR POWER
(pages 38–40)

1. Prometheus Institute and Greentech Media, *PV News*, April 2008, p. 6.

2. Data for 2007 from ibid., p. 7; cumulative number is Worldwatch calculation based on data from Paul Maycock and Prometheus Institute, *PV News*, various issues, and from Travis Bradford, Prometheus Institute, discussion with author, 29 April 2008; 3 million homes is based on 9,100 megawatts and is from European Photovoltaic Industry Association (EPIA), "Global Solar PV Market Estimated at 2.3 GWp in 2007," press release (Brussels: 17 December 2007).

3. Sevenfold is Worldwatch calculation based on Prometheus Institute and Greentech Media, op. cit. note 1, p. 6; fivefold is Worldwatch calculation based on data from Maycock and Prometheus Institute, op. cit. note 2, and on Bradford, op. cit. note 2.

4. Prometheus Institute and Greentech Media, op. cit. note 1, p. 6.

5. Employment from Thomas Chrometzka, "Solar Energy in Germany—Market and Industry," German Solar Industry Association (BSW-Solar), PowerPoint presentation for Washington International Renewable Energy Conference, 6 March 2008, e-mail to author, 11 March 2008; Q-Cells from Travis Bradford, "World PV Market Update and Photovoltaic Markets, Technology, Performance, and Cost to 2015," Prometheus Institute, PowerPoint presentation, e-mail to author, 16 April 2008.

6. EPIA, op. cit. note 2; Chrometzka, op. cit. note 5.

7. Additions from EPIA, "Global Market Outlook for Photovoltaics until 2012: Facing a Sunny Future," Brussels, p. 5, at www.epia.org/fileadmin/EPIA _docs/publications/epia/EPIA__MarketPublication _18feb.pdf, and from Bradford, op. cit. note 2; total from Chrometzka, op. cit. note 5.

8. Jane Burgermeister, "Ultra Thin Solar Modules to Make 2008 Debut in Germany," RenewableEnergy-World.com, 7 September 2007.

9. Ibid.

10. Bradford, op. cit. note 5.

11. Supply constraints from ibid.; Japan's shares are Worldwatch calculations based on Prometheus Institute and Greentech Media, op. cit. note 1, p. 6.

12. Travis Bradford, Prometheus Institute, discussion with author, 16 April 2008.

13. EPIA, op. cit. note 7.

14. Bradford, op. cit. note 5.

15. Ibid.; Prometheus Institute and Greentech Media, op. cit. note 1, p. 6.

16. BSW and EPIA, cited in Chrometzka, op. cit. note 5.

17. Bradford, op. cit. note 5.

18. Calculated by Worldwatch with data from Prometheus Institute and Greentech Media, op. cit. note 1, p. 6, and from Bradford, op. cit. note 5.

19. Figure of 425 megawatts from BSW and EPIA, cited in Chrometzka, op. cit. note 5; 640 megawatts from "Solarbuzz Reports World Solar Photovoltaic Market Growth of 62% in 2007," SolarBuzz.com, 2008; fewer than 100 from Bradford, op. cit. note 12.

20. "Solarbuzz Reports World Solar Photovoltaic Market Growth," op. cit. note 19.

21. Feed-in tariff from Brandon Reed, "Photovoltaic Solar Power Grows Fast in Spain," *Reuters*, 10 October 2007.

22. Prometheus Institute and Greentech Media, op. cit. note 1, p. 6.

23. Ibid.

24. Bradford, op. cit. note 12.

25. Prometheus Institute and Solar Energy Industries Association (SEIA), *US Solar Industry Year in Review—2007* (Cambridge, MA, and Washington, DC: 2008), pp. 1, 4.

26. Bradford, op. cit. note 12; "Whispers of a New Direction: First National Feed-in Tariff Legislation to Be Introduced in US Congress," *Photon International*,

April 2008, p. 45.

27. Utilities recognize value from Bradford, op. cit. note 5; "Southern California Edison Plans Country's Largest Solar Project," GreenBiz.com, 28 March 2008.

28. For Italy, 25 megawatts from BSW and EPIA, cited in Chrometzka, op. cit. note 5; 50 megawatts in Italy from EPIA, op. cit. note 2; South Korea and France from ibid. and from BSW and EPIA, cited in Chrometzka, op. cit. note 5.

29. BSW and EPIA, cited in Chrometzka, op. cit. note 5.

30. Johannes Beck, "Giant Solar Power Station Opened in Portugal," *New Energy*, June 2007, p. 10.

31. Bradford, op. cit. note 5.

32. Second half of 2008 from Bradford, op. cit. note 5.

33. Projection from EPIA, op. cit. note 2; 2007 total from Prometheus Institute and Greentech Media, op. cit. note 1, p. 7.

34. Bradford, op. cit. note 12; "Trina Solar Discontinues Development of Polysilicon Production Facility," press release (Changzhou, China: April 14).

35. U.S. National Renewable Energy Laboratory, "Record Makes Thin-Film Solar Cell Competitive with Silicon Efficiency," press release (Golden, CO: 24 March 2008); J. Peter Lynch, "2007: The Year of the Thin Film PV Stock," RenewableEnergyWorld.com, 2 May 2007.

36. U.S. National Renewable Energy Laboratory, op. cit. note 35.

37. Fourfold increase calculated by Worldwatch with data from Bradford, op. cit. note 5; more than 10 percent from ibid.

38. Limited performance data from Stefan Schmitz, "Financing PV—The Fundamentals," *Refocus Weekly*, 16 January 2008.

39. Increase from 9 to 10 percent from Ken Zweibel, James Mason, and Vasilis Fthenakis, "By 2050 Solar Power Could End U.S. Dependence on Foreign Oil and Slash Greenhouse Gas Emissions," *Scientific American*, January 2008, p. 66; researchers in 2008 from U.S. National Renewable Energy Laboratory, op. cit. note 35.

40. Schmitz, op. cit. note 38; Prometheus Institute and SEIA, op. cit. note 25, p. 5.

41. "Clean Energy Investment 'Breaks the US$100bn Barrier' in 2007," *Refocus Weekly*, 16 January 2008.

42. Schmitz, op. cit. note 38.

43. "Dyed Solar Cells May Offer Unique Installations Opportunities," RenewableEnergyWorld.com, 4 February 2008.

44. Scott Sklar, The Stella Group, Ltd., discussion with author, 30 April 2008; "Konarka Tests Inkjet Printed Solar Cells," RenewableEnergyWorld.com, 5 March 2008.

45. "PV You Can Drive On: Promising Technology in Solar Roads," RenewableEnergyWorld.com, 6 March 2008.

46. Prometheus Institute and Greentech Media, op. cit. note 1, p. 8.

47. Ibid., p. 7.

48. Peter Marsh, "The Sun Shines on the Solar Industry's Quest for 'Grid Parity'," *Financial Times*, 11 January 2008; Sascha Rentzing, "Sun Aplenty," *New Energy*, June 2007, p. 48.

49. Bradford, op. cit. note 5.

50. Jaffray quoted in Rentzing, op. cit. note 48, p. 53.

51. Ibid.

VEHICLE PRODUCTION RISES, BUT FEW CARS ARE "GREEN" (pages 41–43)

1. Colin Couchman, Global Insight Automotive Group, London, e-mail to author, 20 May 2008.

2. Ibid.

3. Ibid.

4. PricewaterhouseCoopers, "Autofacts Global Automotive Outlook, 2008 Q2 Release," www.autofacts.com/data.asp, viewed 11 May 2008.

5. Couchman, op. cit. note 1.

6. Ibid.

7. Ibid.

8. Ibid.

9. Ibid.

10. Figures for 2008 and 2000 from ibid.; 1950 from Motor Vehicle Manufacturers Association, *World Motor Vehicle Data 2005* (Detroit, 2005).

11. "Competition for China's Auto Market is Heating up," *China Daily*: 22 April 2008.

12. "Tata 'NANO'—the People's Car from Tata Motors," at www.tatapeoplescar.com/tatamotors; Michael Renner, "Nano Hypocrisy?" *Eye on Earth* (Worldwatch Institute, 16 January 2008).

13. T. Barker et al., "Technical Summary," in Intergovernmental Panel on Climate Change, *Climate Change 2007: Mitigation. Contribution of Working Group III to the Fourth Assessment Report* (New York: Cambridge University Press, 2007), pp. 48–49.

14. Ibid.

15. Therese Langer and Daniel Williams, *Greener Fleets: Fuel Economy Progress and Prospects* (Washington, DC: American Council for an Energy-Efficient Economy, December 2002).

16. Japan Automobile Manufacturers Association, *2006 Report on Environmental Protection* (Tokyo: October 2006).

17. Ibid.; "Emission Norms," Society of Indian Automobile Manufacturers, at www.siamindia.com/scripts/emission-standards.aspx, viewed 28 November 2007.

18. PricewaterhouseCoopers, op. cit. note 4.

19. Ibid.

20. Toyota Hybrid Synergy View, "One Millionth Hybrid Vehicle Hits the American Road," at www.toyota.com/dyncon/2008/may/road.html?siteid=news_may08h_1.

21. Ibid.

22. U.S. Environmental Protection Agency (EPA), *Light-Duty Automotive Technology and Fuel Economy Trends: 1975 through 2007* (Washington, DC: September 2007), p. ii.

23. Alan Baum, "Market Penetration of Hybrid and Diesel Vehicles in the U.S. Market, 2004–2015," presentation to the Fuel Economy Technology Trends and Policy Options Forum, Washington, DC, 1 October 2007.

24. Calculated from Japan Automobile Manufacturers Association, "Low-Emission Vehicle Shipments 2006," 5 October 2007, at www.jama-english.jp/statistics/low_emission/2006/071005.html.

25. European Automobile Manufacturers' Association, "Diesel is Doing a Lot to Reduce CO_2 Emissions in Europe," at www.acea.be/index.php/news/news_detail/diesel_is_doing_a_lot_to_reduce_co2_emissions_in_europe, viewed 22 November 2007.

26. Michael P. Walsh, *Car Lines*, February 2008, p. 49.

27. Corinna Kester, "Diesels versus Hybrids: Comparing the Environmental Costs," *World Watch*, July/August 2005, p. 21; "ACEEE Releases 'Meanest' and 'Greenest' Vehicle Scorecard," *Clean Edge News*, 26 February 2008.

28. International Council on Clean Transportation, *Passenger Vehicle Greenhouse Gas and Fuel Economy Standards: A Global Update* (Washington, DC: 2007), pp. 8–9.

29. Ibid.

30. European Commission, "Objectives of the Agreements Concluded with the Automobile Industry," at ec.europa.eu/environment/co2/co2_agreements.htm, updated 19 January 2007.

31. Ibid.

32. Percentages calculated from Commission of the European Communities, "Commission Staff Working Document: Accompanying Document to the Communication from the Commission to the Council and the European Parliament, Implementing the Community Strategy to Reduce CO2 Emissions from Cars: Sixth Annual Communication on the Effectiveness of the Strategy" (Brussels: 24 August 2006), p. 22.

33. Ibid., pp. 42, 66.

34. European Environment Agency, *Climate for a Transport Change*, EEA Report No. 1/2008 (Copenhagen: March 2008), p. 23.

35. EPA, op. cit. note 22, p. v.

36. Calculated from ibid., Appendix C: Fuel Economy Distribution Data.

37. Ibid.

38. Ibid.

39. Toyota Motor North America, *2007 North America Environmental Report* (Washington, DC: 2007), p. 15.

40. Author's calculation, based on Commission of the European Communities, op. cit. note 32, on International Organization of Motor Vehicles Manufacturers, at oica.net/category/economic-contributions/auto-jobs, on European Automobile Manufacturers' Association, "Europe Has More Than 250 Automobile Production Sites," at www.acea.be/index.php/news/news_detail/europe_has_more_than_250_automobile_production_sites, viewed 22 November 2007, and on Stacy C. Davis and Susan W. Diegel, *Transportation Energy Data Book: Edition 26* (Oak Ridge, TN: Center for Transportation Analysis, Oak Ridge National Laboratory, 2007), Table 10.15. These numbers represent rough estimates only. Due to a lack of detailed data, they do not distinguish between domestic production and imports, which may distort the results.

41. Boom and recent slump in demand from "Thailand's Eco-Drive," *The Economist*, 21 June 2007; Thai vehicle production and employment from International Organization of Motor Vehicles Manufacturers, op. cit. note 40.

42. "Thailand's Eco-Drive," op. cit. note 41.

43. Ibid.

44. International Organization of Motor Vehicles Manufacturers, at oica.net/category/production-statistics and at oica.net/category/economic-contributions/auto-jobs, viewed 8 December 2007.

45. "Thailand Making Incentives for Eco-Cars," *Associated Press*, 7 December 2007.

46. Employment figures from International Organization of Motor Vehicles Manufacturers, op. cit. note 40.

47. Chery fuel economy from "Thailand's Eco-Drive," op. cit. note 41.

NUCLEAR POWER CRAWLING FORWARD
(pages 44–46)

1. Installed nuclear capacity is defined as reactors connected to the grid as of 31 December 2007 and is based on the Worldwatch Institute database compiled from statistics from International Atomic Energy Agency (IAEA), *Power Reactor Information System*, at www.iaea.org/programmes/a2.

2. IAEA, op. cit. note 1.

3. U.S. Department of Energy, Energy Efficiency & Renewable Energy, "Global Wind Energy Capacity Increases 27% in 2007," *EERE NEWS*, 6 February 2008.

4. Peter Kaplan, "Report Says Developing Countries Eye Nuclear Power," *Reuters*, 12 May 2008; James Kanter, "International Agency Urges the Start of an Energy Revolution," *New York Times*, 8 June 2008.

5. IAEA, op. cit. note 1.

6. Based on Worldwatch Institute database compiled from statistics from IAEA, op. cit. note 1.

7. IAEA, op. cit. note 1.

8. Based on Worldwatch Institute data base compiled from statistics from IAEA, op. cit. note 1.

9. Mycle Schneider with Antony Froggat, *The World Nuclear Industry Status Report 2007* (Brussels: The Greens–European Free Alliance in the European Parliament, January 2008), pp. 7–8.

10. IAEA, op. cit. note 1.

11. Ibid.

12. Ibid.; Schneider with Froggat, op. cit. note 9, p. 37; World Nuclear Association, "Information Paper: Plans for New Nuclear Reactors Worldwide," March 2008, at www.world-nuclear.org/info/inf17.html.

13. Schneider with Froggat, op. cit. note 9, p. 34.

14. World Nuclear Association, "Information Paper: Fast Neutron Reactors," February 2008, at www.world -nuclear.org/info/inf98.html.

15. Bjorn Carey, "A Floating Chernobyl?" *Popular Science*, 10 October 2006, at www.popsci.com.

16. Schneider with Froggat, op. cit. note 9, pp. 29–31.

17. IAEA, op. cit. note 1.

18. Ibid.

19. Ibid.

20. Ibid.; Schneider with Froggat, op. cit. note 9, pp. 7–8.

21. Alan Katz, "Nuclear Bid to Rival Coal Chilled by Flaws, Delay in Finland," *Bloomberg News*, 4 September 2007.

22. James Etheridge, "TVO Says Won't Share Nuclear Reactor Cost Overruns with Areva," *Thomson Financial News*, 28 September 2007.

23. Katz, op. cit. note 21.

24. John Tagliabue, "China Deal Gives Lift to Revival of Fission," *New York Times*, 26 November 2007.

25. Katz, op. cit. note 21.

26. Ibid.

27. "Japan Nuke Plant Leak Bigger than Thought," *Associated Press*, 18 July 2007; Schneider with Froggat, op. cit. note 9, p. 23.

28. "Nuclear Generation Drops 1.9% in 2007," *World Nuclear News*, 9 June 2008, at www.world-nuclear -news.org.

29. Schneider with Froggat, op. cit. note 9, p. 23.

30. IAEA, op. cit. note 1.

31. Dan Murphy, "Middle East Racing to Nuclear Power," *Christian Science Monitor*, 1 November 2007.

32. William Broad and David E. Sanger, "With Eye on Iran, Rivals Also Want Nuclear Power," *New York Times*, 15 April 2007.

33. Duncan Mansfield, "US Nuclear Revival Begins with Restart of TVA's Oldest Reactor," *Associated Press*, 6 May 2007; "Watts Bar Nuclear Plant," Tennessee Valley Authority, at www.tva.gov/sites/wattsbarnuc.htm.

34. U.S. Nuclear Regulatory Commission, "Expected New Nuclear Power Plant Applications," updated 4 June 2008, at www.nrc.gov/reactors/new-licensing/new-licensing-files/expected-new-rx-applications.pdf.

35. Edmund L. Andrews and Matthew Wald, "Energy Bill Aids Expansion of Atomic Power," *New York Times*, 31 July 2007.

36. Moody's Global Credit Research, "New Nuclear Generation in the United States: Keeping Options Open vs. Addressing an Inevitable Necessity," October 2007.

37. Ibid.

38. Ibid.

39. Asjylyn Loder, "Nuclear Power Costs Surge in Rush to Build: Customers May Help Shoulder the Increase," *St. Petersburg Times*, 12 December 2007.

40. William J. Fehrman, President and Chief Nuclear Officer, MidAmerican Nuclear Energy Company, "RE: Withdrawal from Consideration and Return of Letter of Intent Submitted to NRC August 28, 2007," to David B. Matthews, Director, Division of New Reactor Licensing, U.S. Nuclear Regulatory Commission, 5 December 2007.

41. Scott DiSavino, "MidAmerican Drops Idaho Nuclear Project Due to Cost," *Reuters*, 29 January 2008.

STRONG GROWTH IN COMPACT FLUORESCENT BULBS REDUCES ELECTRICITY DEMAND
(pages 47–49)

1. Peter Du Pont, "Asian Energy Trends and Prospects for Energy Efficiency," U.S. Agency for International Development ECO-Asia presentation at TBLI Asia Conference, Bangkok, Thailand, 29 May 2008.
2. Michael Scholand, "Compact Fluorescents Set Record," in Worldwatch Institute, *Vital Signs 2002* (New York: W. W. Norton & Company, 2002), pp. 46–47; International Energy Agency (IEA), *Light's Labor Lost: Policies for Energy-Efficient Lighting* (Paris: 2006), p. 262.
3. David Ryan, Energy Star, U.S. Environmental Protection Agency (EPA), e-mail to Nathan Swire, Worldwatch Institute, 25 August 2008. Data based on trade information from the U.S. International Trade Commission.
4. Paolo Bertoldi, "Residential Lighting Consumption and Saving Potential in the Enlarged EU," European Union Joint Research Center presentation, Paris, 26 February 2007.
5. EPA, "EPA and DOE Spread a Bright Idea: Energy Star Light Bulbs Are Helping to Change the World," press release (Washington, DC: 15 January 2008).
6. Pacific Northwest National Laboratory, *Compact Fluorescent Lighting in America: Lessons Learned on the Way to Market*, prepared for U.S. Department of Energy (DOE), Office of Energy Efficiency and Renewable Energy Building Technologies Program (Richland, WA: 2006), p. 1.3.
7. IEA, op. cit. note 2, p. 262.
8. EPA and DOE Energy Star program, "Energy Star Change a Light, Change the World 2007 Campaign Facts and Assumptions Sheet," flyer, 23 April 2007.
9. Ibid.
10. Ibid.
11. IEA, op. cit. note 2, p. 25.
12. Andy Coghlan, "It's Lights Out for Classic Household Bulb," *New Scientist*, 2 March 2007, pp. 26–27; calculation based on carbon dioxide estimates of 5.2 tons per vehicle per year, in EPA, "Greenhouse Gas Emissions from a Typical Passenger Vehicle," flyer (Washington, DC: February 2005).
13. IEA, op. cit. note 2, pp. 389, 421; Energy Information Administration, *Emissions of Greenhouse Gases Report* (Washington, DC: DOE, 2007).
14. Alana Herro, "World Governments Adopting Bright Idea," *Eye on Earth* (Worldwatch Institute), 5 March 2007.
15. "Europe to Ban Energy-Wasting Light Bulbs," *Der Spiegel Online*, 18 June 2008; Paul Hoskins, "Ireland Goes Green with Light Bulb Rules and Car Tax," *Reuters*, 6 December 2007; "Lights to Go Out on Inefficient Bulbs by 2012," *Canadian Broadcasting Corporation*, 25 April 2007.
16. Paul Davidson, "It's Lights Out for Traditional Light Bulbs," *USA Today*, 16 December 2007.
17. Du Pont, op. cit. note 1.
18. Gregory M. Lamb, "Bulb Brilliance at Wal-Mart as CFLs Go Mainstream," *Christian Science Monitor*, 4 October 2007.
19. Energy Lighting Initiative, "Learn About ELI Website," at www.efficientlighting.net/index.php?option=com_content&task=view&id=18&Itemid=41.
20. Ibid.
21. Energy Star, "Frequently Asked Questions: Information on Compact Fluorescent Light Bulbs (CFLs) and Mercury," flyer (Washington, DC: June 2008).
22. Ibid.
23. Ibid.
24. Coghlan, op. cit. note 12.
25. Ibid.
26. Ibid.
27. Emma Ritch, "LED Global Market Should Keep Getting Brighter and Brighter," *Silicon Valley/San Jose Business Journal*, 11 January 2008.

ONE TWELFTH OF GLOBAL ELECTRICITY COMES FROM COMBINED HEAT AND POWER SYSTEMS
(pages 50–52)

1. Worldwatch calculations based on International Energy Agency (IEA), *Combined Heat and Power: Evaluating the Benefits of Greater Global Investment* (Paris: 2008), on Energy Information Administration, U.S. Department of Energy, Table 6.4 from *International Energy Annual 2005* (Washington, DC: 4 September 2007), and on Sytze Dijkstra, Delta Energy & Environment, e-mail to author, 3 October 2008.
2. Worldwatch calculations, op. cit. note 1.
3. Perrin Quarles Associates, Inc., *Review of Potential Efficiency Improvements at Coal-Fired Power Plants* (Charlottesville, VA: 2001).
4. Low estimate from IEA, op. cit. note 1, p. 10; high estimate from IEA, *Energy Technology Perspectives* (Paris: 2008), p. 263.
5. IEA, op. cit. note 1, p. 10.
6. U.S. Environmental Protection Agency (EPA), Com-

bined Heat and Power Partnership, *Catalog of CHP Technologies* (Washington, DC: 2002), p. 2; Owen Bailey et al., *An Engineering-Economic Analysis of Combined Heat and Power Technologies in a µGrid Application* (Berkeley, CA: Lawrence Berkeley National Laboratory, 2002), pp. 3–5.

7. National Climate Change Committee, Singapore, "District Cooling," at www.nccc.gov.sg/building/dcs.shtm; IEA, "District Heating and Cooling," at www.iea.org/g8/chp/DHC.asp.

8. Bailey et al., op. cit. note 6.

9. IEA, op. cit. note 1, p. 11.

10. IEA, International CHP/DHC Collaborative, *CHP/DHC Country Scorecard: Finland* (Paris: 2008).

11. Gilbert M. Masters, *Renewable and Efficient Electric Power Systems* (Hoboken, NJ: John Wiley & Sons, 2004), pp. 127–28.

12. IEA, op. cit. note 1, p. 11.

13. Worldwatch calculations, op. cit. note 1.

14. IEA, op. cit. note 4, pp. 264–66, 307–31.

15. Ibid., pp. 264–66.

16. Dijkstra, op. cit. note 1; IEA, International CHP/DHC Collaborative, *CHP/DHC Country Scorecard: Denmark* (Paris: 2008), pp. 4–7.

17. Dijkstra, op. cit. note 1; IEA, International CHP/DHC Collaborative, *CHP/DHC Country Scorecard: Germany* (Paris: 2008), p. 10.

18. IEA, op. cit. note 1, pp. 3, 8.

19. Worldwatch calculation, op. cit. note 1.

20. "District Heating and Cooling: Environmental Technology for the 21st Century," policy paper for IEA Executive Committee for the Implementing Agreement on District Heating and Cooling Paper, Copenhagen, 16 May 2002, p. 2; Danish Energy Agency, "Denmark Supports Renewable Energy and District Heating in Russia," press release (Copenhagen: 8 September 2008); Siemens, "Siemens to Supply CHP Plant to Russia," press release (Erlangen, Germany: 17 January 2008).

21. Dijkstra, op. cit. note 1.

22. IEA, op. cit. note 4.

23. Bruce Hedman, "The Role of CHP in the Nation's Energy System," Energy and Environmental Analysis, Inc., presentation at U.S. Clean Heat and Power Association annual meeting, 3 October 2007.

24. Electricity generation from Dijkstra, op. cit. note 1; urban central heating from Tom Kerr, "Sustainable Energy in China: The Role of CHP and District Heating/Cooling," IEA presentation at Danish Sustainable Development Seminar (Beijing: 10 September 2007).

25. EPA, *Facilitating Deployment of Highly Efficient Combined Heat and Power Applications in China: Analysis and Recommendations* (Washington, DC: 2008), p. 12; China from National Development and Reform Commission, *2010 CHP Development Planning and 2020 Development Goal* (Beijing: 2003).

26. IEA, op. cit. note 1, pp. 19–20.

27. IEA, op. cit. note 10.

28. Henry Manczyk and Michael D. Leach, "Combined Heat and Power Generation and District Heating in Denmark: History, Goals, and Technology," at www.energy.rochester.edu/dk/manczyk/denmark.pdf; Birger Lauersen, *Denmark—Answer to a Burning Platform: CHP/DHC* (Paris: IEA, International CHP/DHC Collaborative, 2008); Ture Hammar, *The Case of CHP in Denmark—and Perspectives to Other Countries* (Paris: Organisation for Economic Co-operation and Development and Danish Energy Agency, 1999); Germany from IEA, op. cit. note 17, p. 6; U.S. from IEA, op. cit. note 23, p. 3.

29. IEA, op. cit. note 16, p. 8.

30. Manczyk and Leach, op. cit. note 28; Lauersen, op. cit. note 28; Hammar, op. cit. note 28; Germany from IEA, op. cit. note 17, p. 7.

31. Finland from IEA, op. cit. note 10; Denmark from Lauersen, op. cit. note 28, from Manczyk and Leach, op. cit. note 28, and from IEA, op. cit. note 16, p. 8; Netherlands and Germany from IEA, *Combined Heat & Power and Emissions Trading: Options for Policymakers*, Information Paper (Paris: 2008), pp. 15–16.

32. IEA, op. cit. note 23, p. 9; U.S. Department of Energy, "CHP Regional Application Centers (RACs)," at www.eere.energy.gov/de/chp/chp_applications/chp_application_centers.html; EPA, "Combined Heat and Power Partnership—US EPA," at www.epa.gov/CHP.

33. Thomas Casten, "Recycling Energy to Reduce Costs and Mitigate Climate Change," in Michael MacCracken, Frances Moore, and John C. Topping, Jr., eds., *Sudden and Disruptive Climate Change* (Sterling, VA: Earthscan, 2008).

34. EPA, *Combined Heat and Power Market Potential for Opportunity Fuels* (Washington, DC: 2004), pp. 75–106.

35. IEA, op. cit. note 1, p. 25.

36. Ibid., pp. 22–23.

37. IEA, op. cit. note 4, pp. 264–66; IEA, op. cit. note 16, pp. 10–11; Thomas Casten, *Deploying Clean Energy: Overcoming Regulatory Barriers* (Westmont, IL: Recycled Energy Development, September 2008).

38. European Parliament, Directive 2004/8/EC of the European Parliament and of the Council of 11 February 2004 on the Promotion of Cogeneration Based on a Useful Heat Demand in the Internal Energy Market and Amending Directive 92/42/EEC.

39. Group of Eight Nations, "Growth and Development in the World Economy," 2007 G8 Heiligendamm Summit Declaration, pp. 24–25.

BICYCLE PRODUCTION REACHES 130 MILLION UNITS (pages 53–54)

1. United Nations, *The Growth of World Industry, 1969 Edition, Vol. II* (New York: 1971); United Nations, *Yearbook of Industrial Statistics, 1979 and 1989 Editions, Vol. II* (New York: 1981 and 1991); *Interbike Directory*, various years; United Nations, *Industrial Commodity Statistics Yearbook*, various years; Japan Bicycle Promotion Institute, various years; *Bicycle Retailer and Industry News*, various years.

2. United Nations, *The Growth of World Industry*, op. cit. note 1; United Nations, *Yearbooks of Industrial Statistics*, op. cit. note 1; *Interbike Directory*, op. cit. note 1; United Nations, *Industrial Commodity Statistics Yearbook,* op. cit. note 1; Japan Bicycle Promotion Institute, op. cit. note 1; *Bicycle Retailer and Industry News*, op. cit. note 1.

3. United Nations, *The Growth of World Industry*, op. cit. note 1; United Nations, *Yearbooks of Industrial Statistics*, op. cit. note 1; *Interbike Directory*, op. cit. note 1; United Nations, *Industrial Commodity Statistics Yearbook,* op. cit. note 1; Japan Bicycle Promotion Institute, op. cit. note 1; *Bicycle Retailer and Industry News*, op. cit. note 1.

4. Jonathan X. Weinert et al., "The Transition to Electric Bikes in China: Effect on Travel Behavior, Mode Shift, and User: Safety Perceptions in a Medium-Sized City," paper presented to 86th Annual Meeting, Transportation Research Board, 31 July 2006.

5. John Pucher and Ralph Buehler, "Making Cycling Irresistible: Lessons from the Netherlands, Denmark, and Germany," *Transport Reviews*, July 2008, pp. 495–528.

6. Ibid.

7. V. Setty Pendakur, "Non-Motorized Transport in African Cities: Lessons from Experience in Kenya and Tanzania," SSATP Working Paper No. 80 (Washington, DC: World Bank, 2005).

8. John Crenshaw and Doug McClellan, "China Remains on Top Despite Pressures," *Bicycle Retailer*

and Industry News, 1 July 2008.

9. Ibid.

10. Bike Europe, "Alarming Rubber Shortage?" at www.bike-eu.com/news, 19 April 2006; Jack Oortwijn, "Rising Retail Prices for Bikes," Bike Europe, at www.bike-eu.com/news, 21 March 2008.

11. Nicole Formosa, "Gas Price Hikes Fuel Sales of Commuter Accessories," *Bicycle Retailer and Industry News*, 1 July 2008, p. 1.

12. Ibid.

13. Dan Nephin, "Tired of Pricey Gas, Police Pump Up Bike Patrols," *Associated Press*, 26 May 2008.

14. Ibid.

15. Pucher and Buehler, op. cit. note 5.

16. Ibid.

17. Ibid.

18. Ibid.

19. Elisabeth Rosenthal, "European Support for Bicycles Promotes Sharing of the Wheels," *New York Times*, 9 November 2008.

20. Steven Erlanger, "A New Fashion Catches On in Paris: Cheap Bicycle Rentals," *New York Times*, 13 July 2008.

21. Ibid.

22. Ibid.

23. John Ward Anderson, "Paris Embraces Plan to Become City of Bikes," *Washington Post,* 24 March 2007.

CLIMATE CHANGE ACCELERATES (pages 56–58)

1. J. Hansen et al., "Global Land-Ocean Temperature Index in .01C, Base Period 1951–1980 (January-December)," Goddard Institute for Space Studies (GISS), at data.giss.nasa.gov/gistemp/tabledata/GLB.Ts+dSST.txt.

2. Ibid.

3. Ibid.; World Meteorological Organization (WMO), *Press Release No. 805* (Geneva: 13 December 2007).

4. GISS, "Global Temperature Trends: 2007 Summation," at data.giss.nasa.gov/gistemp/2007; T. Barker et al., "Summary," in Intergovernmental Panel on Climate Change (IPCC), *Climate Change 2007: Mitigation. Contribution of Working Group III to the Fourth Assessment Report of the Intergovernmental Panel on Climate Change* (New York: Cambridge University Press, 2007), p. 28.

5. C. D. Keeling et al., *Exchanges of Atmospheric CO_2 and $13CO_2$ with the Terrestrial Biosphere and Oceans from 1978 to 2000. I. Global Aspects*, SIO Reference

Series, No. 01-06 (San Diego, CA: Scripps Institution of Oceanography, 2001), with updated data from Stephen Piper, e-mail to Janet Sawin, Worldwatch Institute, 8 February 2008.

6. IPCC, *Climate Change 2007: Synthesis Report* (Geneva: 2007).

7. Ibid.

8. M. Z. Jacobson, *Atmospheric Pollution: History, Science, and Regulation* (Cambridge, U.K.: Cambridge University Press, 2002).

9. G. A. Meehl et al., "2007: Global Climate Projections," in IPCC, *Climate Change 2007: The Physical Science Basis. Contribution of Working Group I to the Fourth Assessment Report of the Intergovernmental Panel on Climate Change* (New York: Cambridge University Press, 2007), p. 822.

10. J. Canadell et al., "Contributions to Accelerating Atmospheric CO_2 Growth from Economic Activity, Carbon Intensity, and Efficiency of Natural Sinks," *Proceedings of the National Academy of Sciences*, September 2007.

11. WMO, op. cit. note 3.

12. Ibid.

13. GISS, op. cit. note 4.

14. National Snow and Ice Data Center, "Arctic Sea Ice Shatters All Previous Record Lows," press release (Boulder, CO: 1 October 2007).

15. L. Stearns and G. Hamilton, "Rapid Volume Loss from Two East Greenland Outlet Glaciers Quantified Using Repeat Stereo Satellite Imagery," *Geophysical Research Letters*, 14 March 2007.

16. E. Rignot et al., "Recent Antarctic Ice Mass Loss from Radar Interferometry and Regional Climate Modeling," *Nature Geoscience*, January 2008.

17. "Summary for Policymakers," in IPCC, op. cit. note 9, p. 7.

18. O. Hoegh-Guldberg et al., "Coral Reefs Under Rapid Climate Change and Ocean Acidification," *Science*, 14 December 2007, pp. 1737–42.

19. Pervaze A. Sheikh et al., "Global Climate Change and Wildlife," prepared for U.S. Congress, Congressional Research Service, U.S. Library of Congress, 12 February 2007, p. CRS-1.

20. Ibid.

21. United Nations, "Security Council Holds First-Ever Debate on Impact of Climate Change on Peace, Security, Hearing over 50 Speakers," press release (New York: 17 April 2007).

22. G8 Summit 2007, "Chair's Summary," Heiligendamm, Germany, 8 June 2007; United Nations, "Ban Ki-moon Convenes Largest-ever Meeting of Global Leaders on Climate Change," press release (New York: 24 September 2007); U.S. Department of State, "Chairman's Summary: First Major Economies Meeting on Energy Security and Climate Change" (Washington, DC: 28 September 2007).

23. U.N. Framework Convention on Climate Change, *Decision /CP.13 Bali Action Plan* (Bonn, Germany: December 2007).

CARBON EMISSIONS ON THE RISE BUT POLICIES GROWING TOO (pages 59–61)

1. Carbon emissions based on G. Marland et al., "Global, Regional, and National Fossil Fuel CO_2 Emissions," in Carbon Dioxide Information Analysis Center (CDIAC), *Trends: A Compendium of Data on Global Change* (Oak Ridge, TN: Oak Ridge National Laboratory, U.S. Department of Energy, 2007), on BP, *Statistical Review of World Energy* (London: 2008), and on U.S. Energy Information Administration (EIA), "U.S. Carbon Dioxide Emissions from Energy Sources 2007 Flash Estimate," at www.eia.doe.gov/oiaf/1605/flash/flash.html, viewed May 2008.

2. Ibid.

3. Ibid.

4. Ibid.

5. Ibid.

6. M. Z. Jacobson, *Atmospheric Pollution; History, Science and Regulation* (Cambridge, U.K.: Cambridge University Press, 2002).

7. "Summary for Policymakers," in Intergovernmental Panel on Climate Change (IPCC), *Climate Change 2007: Synthesis Report of the Fourth Assessment Report of the Intergovernmental Panel on Climate Change* (New York: Cambridge University Press, 2007).

8. Based on Marland et al., op. cit. note 1, on BP, op. cit. note 1, on EIA, op. cit. note 1, and on "Technical Summary," in IPCC, *Climate Change 2007: Mitigation. Contribution of Working Group III to the Fourth Assessment Report of the Intergovernmental Panel on Climate Change* (New York: Cambridge University Press, 2007).

9. Oak Ridge National Laboratory, "Bioenergy Conversion Factors," at bioenergy.ornl.gov/papers/misc/energy_conv.html.

10. Based on Marland et al., op. cit. note 1, on BP, op. cit. note 1, on EIA, op. cit. note 1, and on IPCC, op. cit. note 8.

11. Adam R. Brandt and Alexander E. Farrell, "Scraping

the Bottom of the Barrel: Greenhouse Gas Emission Consequences of a Transition to Low-quality and Synthetic Petroleum Resources," *Climatic Change*, October 2007, pp. 241–63.

12. D. Woynillowicz, "Tar Sands Fever," *Worldwatch Magazine*, September/October 2007.

13. Ibid.

14. Marland et al., op. cit. note 1; C. D. Keeling et al., *Exchanges of Atmospheric CO_2 and $13CO_2$ with the Terrestrial Biosphere and Oceans from 1978 to 2000. I. Global Aspects*, SIO Reference Series (San Diego, CA: Scripps Institution of Oceanography, 2001).

15. Based on primary energy consumption from BP, op. cit. note 1.

16. Based on Marland et al., op. cit. note 1, on BP, op. cit. note 1, and on EIA, op. cit. note 1.

17. Christopher Flavin, "Building a Low-Carbon Economy," in Worldwatch Institute, *State of the World 2008* (New York: W. W. Norton & Company, 2008), pp. 75–90.

18. Janet Sawin, "Germany Leads Way on Renewables, Sets 45% Target by 2030," Worldwatch Institute, at www.worldwatch.org/node/5430.

19. McKinsey & Company, *Reducing U.S. Greenhouse Gas Emissions: How Much at What Cost?* (November 2007); see also James Russell, "Coal Use Rises Dramatically Despite Impacts on Climate and Health," *Vital Signs Online*, Worldwatch Institute, November 2007.

20. United Nations, *Report of the Conference of the Parties on its Thirteenth Session, Held in Bali from 3 to 15 December 2007*, U.N. Framework Convention on Climate Change, March 2008.

21. United Nations, *Kyoto Protocol to the United Nations Framework Convention on Climate Change*, 1998.

22. Ibid.; United Nations, "Kyoto Protocol; Status of Ratification," U.N. Framework Convention on Climate Change, May 2008.

23. A. D. Ellerman and P. L. Joskow, *The European Unions' Emissions Trading System in Perspective* (Arlington, VA: Pew Center on Global Climate Change, May 2008).

24. Ibid.

25. "Impact Assessment," in Commission of the European Communities, *Package of Implementation Measures for the EU's Objectives on Climate Change and Renewable Energy for 2020* (Brussels: January 2008).

26. Ibid.

27. Office of Joe Lieberman, "Majority of Senators Step Forward to Support Mandatory, Comprehensive Climate Legislation," press release (Washington, DC: 6 June 2008).

28. Pew Center on Global Climate Change, "Greenhouse Gas Emissions Targets," at www.pewclimate.org/what_s_being_done/in_the_states/emissionstargets_map.cfm.

29. California Air Resource Board, "Climate Change Draft Scoping Plan: A Framework for Change," discussion draft (Sacramento, CA: June 2008).

30. Asia Pacific Energy Research Centre, *APEC Energy Overview 2007* (Tokyo: January 2008).

31. Ibid.

32. U.N. Environment Programme (UNEP), "UNEP Unveils the Climate Neutral Network to Catalyze a Transition to a Low Carbon World," press release (Nairobi: 21 February 2008).

33. UNEP Finance Initiative, *CEO Briefing: Carbon Crunch, Meeting the Cost* (Nairobi: December 2007).

34. IPCC, op. cit. note 8.

35. J. Jowit and P. Wintour, "Cost of Tackling Global Climate Change Has Doubled, Warns Stern," (London) *The Guardian*, 26 June 2008.

36. Nicholas Stern, *The Economics of Climate Change: The Stern Review* (Cambridge, U.K.: Cambridge University Press, 2007).

WEATHER-RELATED DISASTERS DOMINATE (pages 62–64)

1. Munich Re, *Topics Geo: Natural Catastrophes 2007—Analyses, Assessments, Positions* (Munich: 2008), p. 45.

2. Munich Re calculation, based on NatCatSERVICE database, 2008.

3. Centre for Research on the Epidemiology of Disasters (CRED), "Disaster Category Classification for Operational Purposes," consultation meeting, Geneva, 8 June 2007.

4. *CRED, Annual Disaster Statistical Review: Number and Trends 2007* (Brussels: 2008), pp. 40–41.

5. Ibid.

6. Munich Re, op. cit. note 1, p. 45.

7. Ibid., p. 50.

8. Munich Re, op. cit. note 2.

9. Ibid.

10. Ibid.

11. Ibid.

12. Ibid.

13. Munich Re, "Natural Catastrophe Figures for 2007," press release (Munich: 27 December 2007).

14. Joint Typhoon Warning Center, "Northern Indian Ocean Tropical Cyclone Best Track Data: Cyclone

Gonu," Naval Maritime Forecast Center, U.S. Navy, 2007.

15. Munich Re, op. cit. note 1, p. 12.

16. Ibid.

17. National Climatic Data Center (NCDC), *Climate of 2007—In Historical Perspective, Preliminary Annual Report* (Washington, DC: National Oceanic and Atmospheric Administration, December 2007).

18. Munich Re, op. cit. note 2.

19. NCDC, op. cit. note 17.

20. Ibid.

21. Munich Re, op. cit. note 2.

22. Ibid.

23. Ibid.

24. P. Höppe and R. A. Pielke, Jr., eds., *Climate Change and Disaster Losses: Understanding and Attributing Trends and Projections*, Report of a workshop, Hohenkammer, Germany, 25–26 May 2006 (Boulder and Munich: University of Colorado and Munich Re, 2006).

25. Ibid.

26. U.N. Population Fund, *State of World Population 2007* (New York: 2007), p. 1.

27. Ibid.

28. Intergovernmental Panel on Climate Change, *Climate Change 2007, The Physical Science Basis: Summary for Policymakers* (Geneva: 2007).

29. Ibid.

30. Munich Re calculation, based on World Bank Development Data Center, July 2008.

31. Ibid.

32. Ibid.

33. World Bank, Caribbean Catastrophe Risk Insurance Facility, at www.worldbank.org.

GLOBAL ECONOMIC GROWTH CONTINUES AT EXPENSE OF ECOLOGICAL SYSTEMS (pages 66–68)

1. International Monetary Fund (IMF), *World Economic Outlook Database* (Washington, DC: October 2007). Note the 2007 figure is a preliminary estimate from October 2007 and is subject to change. These figures represent inflation-adjusted IMF data.

2. Ibid.

3. IMF, *World Economic Outlook 2007:Globalization and Inequality* (Washington, DC: October 2007), p. xi. Unless otherwise specified, all further analysis is based on PPP terms.

4. IMF, op. cit. note 1.

5. Ibid.

6. IMF, op. cit. note 3, p. 69.

7. Ibid.

8. Ibid.

9. IMF, op. cit. note 1. A recent World Bank analysis of the global economy in 2005 provided a downward revision of China's GDP, determining that in PPP terms China's GDP was 40 percent smaller. These data, however, are limited to 2005 and are not compatible with this broader IMF data set, so they have not been incorporated here. For more information on the revision, see World Bank, "2005 International Comparison Program Preliminary Global Report Compares Size of Economies," press release (Washington, DC: 17 December 2007).

10. IMF, op. cit. note 1.

11. IMF, op. cit. note 3, pp. 83–86.

12. Joseph Kahn and Jim Yardley, "As China Roars, Pollution Reaches Deadly Extremes," *New York Times*, 26 August 2007.

13. Ibid.

14. Sulfur dioxide from ibid.; carbon dioxide from Eric Martinot and Li Junfeng, *Powering China's Development: The Role of Renewable Energy* (Washington, DC: Worldwatch Institute, 2007), p. 10.

15. IMF, op. cit. note 1.

16. Ibid.; IMF, op. cit. note 3, pp. 11, 76–77.

17. IMF, op. cit. note 1.

18. IMF, op. cit. note 3, p. 83.

19. IMF, op. cit. note 1; IMF, op. cit. note 3, pp. 95–97.

20. IMF, op. cit. note 1.

21. Ibid.; U.S. Bureau of the Census, *International Data Base*, electronic database (Suitland, MD: updated 16 July 2007).

22. IMF, op. cit. note 1; Census Bureau, op. cit. note 21.

23. IMF, op. cit. note 1; Census Bureau, op. cit. note 21.

24. U.N. Environment Programme, *Global Environmental Outlook–4: Environment for Development* (Nairobi: 2007), p. 234.

25. Nicholas Stern, *The Economics of Climate Change: The Stern Review* (Cambridge, U.K.: Cambridge University Press, 2007); Frank Ackerman, "Debating Climate Economics: The Stern Review vs. Its Critics," report to Friends of the Earth–UK (Medford, MA: Global Development and Environment Institute at Tufts University, July 2007), p. 2.

26. Millennium Ecosystem Assessment, *Ecosystems and Human Well-being: Synthesis* (Washington, DC: Island Press, 2005); Global Footprint Network, *National Footprint and Biocapacity Accounts*, 2006 edition (Oakland, CA: 2006); World Wide Fund for Nature

(WWF), Zoological Society of London, and Global Footprint Network, *Living Planet Report 2006* (Gland, Switzerland: WWF, 2006).

27. Global Footprint Network, op. cit. note 26.

28. "China Plans to Set Up Green GDP System in 3–5 Years," *China Daily*, 12 March 2004; "Blind Pursuit of GDP to Be Abandoned," *China Daily*, 5 March 2004.

29. Chris Buckley, "China Silences Green GDP Study, Report Says," *Reuters*, 23 July 2007.

30. Ibid.; Kahn and Yardley, op. cit. note 12.

31. John Talberth, Clifford Cobb, and Noah Slattery, *The Genuine Progress Indicator 2006, A Tool for Sustainable Development* (Oakland, CA: Redefining Progress, 2006).

32. Ibid.

33. Yifat Susskind, "11 Solutions to Halting the Environmental Crisis," *AlterNet*, 31 October 2007; Prem Tinsulanonda, President of The Privy Council, "Sufficiency Economy: His Majesty's Philosophy for Development," presentation at Leadership Forum 2001, Bangkok, Thailand, 15 March 2001.

CARBON MARKETS GAIN MOMENTUM, DESPITE CHALLENGES (pages 69–71)

1. Point Carbon, "Global Carbon Market Grows 80% in 2007," press release (Oslo: 18 January 2008). Dollar amount converted from euros using exchange rate for 18 January 2008.

2. World Bank, *State and Trends of the Carbon Market 2007* (Washington, DC: May 2007), p. 3.

3. European Communities, "EU Action Against Climate Change," brochure (Brussels: September 2005), p. 8.

4. Ibid. Euros converted to dollars on 18 January 2008.

5. Ibid.

6. World Bank, op. cit. note 2.

7. Ibid.

8. European Communities, op. cit. note 3, p. 9; European Commission, "Climate Change: Commission Proposes Bringing Air Transport into EU Emissions Trading Scheme," press release (Brussels: 20 December 2006).

9. Alex Dewar et al., *Cap and Trade Policy in the United States* (draft) (Washington, DC: Natural Resources Defense Council, August 2007), p. 12.

10. World Bank, op. cit. note 2.

11. Ibid.

12. Ibid.

13. World Bank, "Forest Carbon Partnership Facility Launched at Bali Climate Meeting," press release (Bali, Indonesia: 11 December 2007).

14. Ibid.

15. Ibid.

16. Katherine Hamilton et al., *State of the Voluntary Carbon Markets 2007: Picking Up Steam* (San Francisco: Ecosystem Marketplace, July 2007), p. 5.

17. Point Carbon, "Carbon Market North America," 16 January 2008, at www.pointcarbon.com, p. 4.

18. This does not include emissions from gas flaring, cement making, or land use change. U.S. carbon dioxide emissions are a Worldwatch calculation from BP, *Statistical Review of World Energy* (London: 2007); U.N. Framework Convention on Climate Change, "Status of Ratification," at unfccc.int, viewed 18 January 2008.

19. Regional Greenhouse Gas Initiative, "About RGGI," at www.rggi.org, viewed 20 July 2007; Point Carbon, op. cit. note 17.

20. Office of the Governor, "Gov. Schwarzenegger Signs Landmark Legislation to Reduce Greenhouse Gas Emissions," press release (27 September 2006); Felicity Barringer, "Officials Reach California Deal to Cut Emissions," *New York Times*, 31 August 2006; Point Carbon, "Carbon Market North America," 1 August 2007, at www.pointcarbon.com.

21. Office of the Governor, op. cit. note 20.

22. Western Climate Initiative, at www.westernclimateinitiative.org, viewed 28 January 2008.

23. Ibid.

JOBS IN RENEWABLE ENERGY EXPANDING (pages 72–74)

1. Michael Renner, Sean Sweeney, and Jill Kubit, *Green Jobs: Towards Decent Work in a Low-Carbon World*, Commissioned by the United Nations Environment Programme for its joint Green Jobs Initiative with the International Labour Organization and the International Trade Union Confederation (Nairobi: UNEP, September 2008).

2. Ibid.

3. Ibid.

4. China from James Kynge, "China Plans to Close Down 25,800 Coal Mines This Year," *Financial Times*, 11 January 1999, and from Erik Eckholm, "Dangerous Coal Mines Take Human Toll in China," *New York Times*, 19 June 2000; U.S. Department of Labor, Bureau of Labor Statistics,

National Employment, Hours, and Earnings, database; Uwe Fritsche et al., *Das Energiewende-Szenario 2020* (Berlin: Öko-Institut, 1996); U.K. Department for Environment, Food and Rural Affairs and Trade Unions Sustainable Development Advisory Committee, *A Fair and Just Transition—Research Report for Greening the Workplace* (London: 2005), p. 28; South Africa from International Labour Organization, *LABORSTA Labour Statistics Database*, viewed 26 October 2007.

5. U.S. Department of Energy, Energy Information Administration, *Annual Energy Review 2006* (Washington, DC: 2007); U.S. Department of Labor, op. cit. note 4.

6. Marlene Kratzat et al., *Erneuerbare Energien: Bruttobeschäftigung 2006* (Stuttgart, Berlin, and Osnabrück: Zentrum für Sonnenenergie und Wasserstoff-Forschung Baden-Württemberg, Deutsches Institut für Wirtschaftsforschung, Deutsches Zentrum für Luft- und Raumfahrt, and Gesellschaft für wirtschaftliche Strukturforschung, 2007).

7. Theo Bühler, Herbert Klemisch, and Krischan Ostenrath, *Ausbildung und Arbeit für erneuerbare Energien. Statusbericht 2007* (Bonn: Wissenschaftsladen Bonn, 2007), p. 4.

8. Joaquín Nieto Sáinz, *Employment Estimates for the Renewable Energy Industry 2007* (Madrid: Instituto Sindical de Trabajo, Ambiente y Salud (ISTAS) and Comisiones Obreras, 2008).

9. "Employment," Danish Wind Industry Association, at www.windpower.org/composite-1456.htm, viewed 17 October 2007.

10. Roger Bezdek, *Renewable Energy and Energy Efficiency: Economic Drivers for the 21st Century* (Boulder, CO: American Solar Energy Society, 2007).

11. Suzlon takeover of REpower from Eric Reguly, "Germany's Green Example Could Be Revolutionary," *The Global and Mail* (Toronto), 28 September 2007.

12. Greenpeace International and Global Wind Energy Council, *Global Wind Energy Outlook 2006* (Amsterdam and Brussels: 2006), p. 12; Raman Thothathri, "The Wind Brought Jobs and Prosperity," *New Energy*, November 1999.

13. Suzlon Energy, "Factsheet," at www.suzlon.com/FactSheet.html?cp=1_4, and "Global Footprint," at www.suzlon.com/Global%20Footprint.html?cp=1_7, both viewed 17 June 2008.

14. Eric Martinot and Li Junfeng, *Powering China's Development: The Role of Renewable Energy* (Washington, DC: Worldwatch Insitute, 2007).

15. Li Junfeng, Deputy Director General of the Energy Research Institute of the National Development and Reform Commission in Beijing, and General Secretary of the Chinese Renewable Energy Industries Association, discussion with Yingling Liu, Worldwatch Institute, 12 November 2007.

16. Ibid.

17. Arne Jacobson and Daniel M. Kammen, "Engineering, Institutions, and the Public Interest: Evaluating Product Quality in the Kenyan Solar Photovoltaics Industry," *Energy Policy*, vol. 35 (2007), pp. 2960–68; Arne Jacobson, "Research for Results: Interdisciplinary Research on Solar Electrification in Kenya," University of California at Berkeley, Renewable and Appropriate Energy Laboratory, undated, at iis-db.stanford.edu/evnts/3920/Jacobson_6nov.pdf.

18. Dipal Chandra Barua, *Grameen Shakti: Pioneering and Expanding Green Energy Revolution to Rural Bangladesh* (Dhaka, Bangladesh: Grameen Bank Bhaban, 2008).

19. Worldwatch Institute, *Biofuels for Transport: Global Potential and Implications for Sustainable Energy and Agriculture* (London: Earthscan, 2007), pp. 124–25; John Rumsey and Jonathan Wheatley, "Poor Practices Taint Brazil's Ethanol Exports," *Financial Times*, 20 May 2008.

20. Malaysian Palm Oil Council, "The Palm Oil," at www.mpoc.org.my/main_palmoil_01.asp.

21. "Trilemmas—Carbon Emissions, Renewable Energy and the Palm Oil Industry," Singapore Institute of International Affairs, at www.siiaonline.org/news_highlights?wid=171&func=viewSubmissions&sid=1389.

22. Rachel Smolker et al., *The Real Cost of Agrofuels: Food, Forest and the Climate* (Amsterdam: Global Forest Coalition, 2007); Richard Doornbosch and Ronald Steenblik, *Biofuels: Is the Cure Worse than the Disease?* prepared for OECD Round Table on Sustainable Development, Paris, 11–12 September 2007.

23. Worldwatch Institute, op. cit. note 19, pp. 124, 126.

24. Oxfam International, "Bio-fuelling Poverty," Oxfam Briefing Note (Oxford, U.K.: 1 November 2007).

25. International Labour Organization, "Indonesian Plantation Workers Still Face Lack of Labour Rights," press release (Jakarta: 26 August 2005).

26. Friends of the Earth, LifeMosaic, and Sawit Watch, *Losing Ground. The Human Rights Impacts of Oil Palm Plantation Expansion in Indonesia* (London, Edinburgh, and Bogor: 2008), p. 77.

27. Ibid., p. 78.
28. John P. Holdren, *Final Report to the William and Flora Hewlett Foundation from the Woods Hole Research Center*, Phase I of a Project on Linking Climate Policy with Development Strategy in Brazil, China, and India (Woods Hole, MA: Woods Hole Research Center, 2007), pp. 198, 319.
29. Ibid.
30. Ibid.
31. Greenpeace International and Global Wind Energy Council, op. cit. note 12.
32. Ibid.
33. European Photovoltaic Industry Association and Greenpeace International, *Solar Generation IV–2007* (Brussels and Amsterdam: 2007).
34. Ibid.

MICROFINANCE SURGING (pages 75–77)

1. Worldwatch calculations based on data in Sam Daley-Harris, *State of the Microcredit Summit Campaign Report 2007* (Washington, DC: Microcredit Summit Campaign), p. 22. Growth rate calculation excludes new borrowers from microfinance institutions (MFIs) that are reporting for the first time.
2. Growth in borrowers from ibid.; growth in global loan portfolio from Microfinance Information Exchange (MIX), "Trend Lines 2004–06 MFI Benchmarks," MIX database, at www.themix.org, viewed 16 June 2008. The Microcredit Summit Campaign compiles participant data from more than 4,000 microfinance institutions worldwide; MIX compiles participant and financial data from 340 MFIs.
3. Maria Otero, "Commentary: Microfinance at the Crossroads," Forbes.com, 19 May 2008.
4. MIX, "2006 MFI Benchmarks," MIX database, www.themix.org, viewed 24 June 2008.
5. Ibid.
6. MIX, op. cit. note 2.
7. Ibid.
8. Number of borrowers from Daley-Harris, op. cit. note 1; loan portfolio and average loan balance from MIX, op. cit. note 2.
9. Daley-Harris, op. cit. note 1.
10. Xavier Reille and Sarah Forster, *Foreign Capital Investment in Microfinance: Balancing Social and Financial Returns*, CGAP Focus Note No. 44 (Washington, DC: Consultative Group to Assist the Poor, February 2008), p. 1.
11. Ibid., p. 15.
12. Ibid.
13. Ibid., p. 3.
14. Ibid., pp. 3–4.
15. Reille and Forster, op. cit. note 10, p. 16.
16. Otero, op. cit. note 3.
17. "Compartamos IPO: Microfinance Doing Good, or the Undoing of Microfinance?" *Microcredit Summit E-News*, July 2007.
18. "The Banco Compartamos Initial Public Offering," *Insight* (Boston: Accion International, June 2007), p. 1.
19. Richard Rosenberg, *CGAP Reflections on the Compartamos Initial Public Offering: A Case Study on Microfinance Interest Rates and Profits* (Washington, DC: Consultative Group to Assist the Poor, June 2007).
20. Ibid.
21. "Remarks by Mohammed Yunus, Managing Director, Grameen Bank," *Microcredit Summit E-News*, July 2007.
22. Rosenberg, op. cit. note 19.
23. Ibid.
24. Daley-Harris, op. cit. note 1, p. 30.
25. Gautam Ivatury and Ignacio Mas, *The Early Experience with Branchless Banking*, Focus Note No. 46 (Washington, DC: Consultative Group to Assist the Poor, April 2008), p. 2.
26. Ibid.
27. Ibid.
28. Worldwatch calculation based on 133 million from Daley-Harris, op. cit. note 1, and on $2 per day from World Bank, "Understanding Poverty," at web.worldbank.org/WBSITE/EXTERNAL/TOPICS/EXTPOVERTY/0,,contentMDK:20153855~menuPK:373757~pagePK:148956~piPK:216618~theSitePK:336992,00.html, viewed 3 July 2008.
29. Malika Anand and Richard Rosenberg, *Are We Overestimating Demand for Microloans?* CGAP Brief (Washington: Consultative Group to Assist the Poor, April 2008).
30. Ibid.
31. Microcredit Summit Campaign, at www.microcreditsummit.org, viewed 3 July 2008.
32. David Lascelles, "Microfinance Banana Skins," *MicroBanking Bulletin*, spring 2008, pp. 1–2.
33. Ibid.

PEACEKEEPING BUDGETS AND PERSONNEL SOAR TO NEW HEIGHTS (pages 80–82)

1. U.N. Department of Public Information (UNDPI), "United Nations Peacekeeping Operations. Back-

ground Note" (New York: 30 November 2007, and earlier editions); Worldwatch database. All dollar amounts are in 2007 dollars.

2. U.N. Department of Peacekeeping Operations (UNDPKO), "Monthly Summary of Contributors," at www.un.org/Depts/dpko/dpko/contributors/index .htm, viewed 14 January 2008; personnel number also based on William Durch, Henry Stimson Center, Washington, DC, e-mail to author, 9 January 1996, and on Global Policy Forum (GPF), at www .globalpolicy.org/security/peacekpg/data/pkomctab .htm, viewed 2 January 2008.

3. UNDPKO, op. cit. note 2.

4. Ibid.

5. UNDPI, op. cit. note 1; UNDPI, "United Nations Political and Peace-Building Missions. Background Note" (New York: 30 November 2007). The political and peacebuilding missions in Afghanistan, Sierra Leone, and Burundi are directed by the UNDPKO; the others, all much smaller, by the U.N. Department of Political Affairs.

6. UNDPKO, "United Nations Peacekeeping Factsheet," (New York: May 2007).

7. Stockholm International Peace Research Institute, "Recent Trends in Military Expenditure," at www .sipri.org/contents/milap/milex/mex_trends.html, viewed 4 January 2008. SIPRI reports $1,204 billion in 2006 terms; in 2007 dollars, this comes to $1,232 billion.

8. Amy Belasco, "The Cost of Iraq, Afghanistan, and Other Global War on Terror Operations Since 9/11," CRS Report for Congress, U.S. Congressional Research Service, updated 9 November 2007, p. 6. In current dollars, the war costs amount to $607 billion. In 2007 dollars, they amount to $632 billion. This covers budget authority from fiscal year 2003 to 2007, plus budget requests for fiscal year 2008.

9. Foreign military deployments from "World Military Deployments," at www.globalsecurity.org/military/ world/deploy.htm, updated 17 May 2005.

10. Ibid.

11. Ibid.

12. Security Council Report, "January 2008—Chad/CAR," at www.securitycouncilreport.org/site/c.glKWLeMTI sG/b.3750591, viewed 3 January 2008.

13. U.N. Security Council, Resolution 1769 (2007), New York, 31 July 2007.

14. "Sudan: Waiting for Peacekeeping Muscle in Darfur," IRIN News, 31 December 2007.

15. UNDPI, op. cit. note 1.

16. Author's calculation, based on data from UNDPKO, op. cit. note 2. The percentage figures in this and the following paragraph refer to peacekeeping personnel excluding civilian staff.

17. Calculated from UNDPKO, op. cit. note 2.

18. Ibid.

19. Ibid.

20. Ibid.

21. UNDPI, op. cit. note 1.

22. Ibid.

23. Ibid.

24. Ibid.

25. Calculated from ibid.

26. Ibid.

27. UNDPKO, op. cit. note 6.

28. Timo Pelz and Volker Lehmann, "The Evolution of UN Peacekeeping (1): Hybrid Missions," fact sheet (New York: Friedrich Ebert Stiftung, November 2007).

29. Ibid.

30. UNDPKO, op. cit. note 6.

31. Ibid.

32. Ibid.

33. GPF, "US vs. Total Debt to the UN: 2007," at www .globalpolicy.org/finance/tables/core/un-us-07.htm, viewed 8 February 2008.

34. GPF, "Debt of 15 Largest Payers to the Peacekeeping Budget 2007," at www.globalpolicy.org/finance/ tables/pko/due2007.htm, viewed 8 February 2008.

35. Ibid.

36. Ibid.

37. Worldwatch Institute database, compiled from Stockholm International Peace Research Institute, at www.sipri.org/contents/conflict/database-Intro, viewed 1 January 2008; from Center for International Peace Operations, Berlin, Germany, www.zif -berlin.org, viewed 2 January 2008; from Future of Peace Operations Program, "Numbers of Uniformed Personnel in Peace Operations at Mid-Year, 1948–2006," undated, supplemental material to William J. Durch and Tobias C. Berkman, Who Should Keep the Peace? Providing Security for Twenty-First-Century Peace Operations (Washington, DC: Henry L. Stimson Center, 2006); and from a broad variety of newspaper articles and other sources.

38. Worldwatch Institute database.

39. Ibid.

40. Ibid.

FERTILITY FALLS, POPULATION RISES, FUTURE UNCERTAIN (pages 83–85)

1. Unless otherwise noted, all demographic data are from U.N. Population Division, Department of Economic and Social Affairs, *World Population Prospects: The 2006 Revision* (New York: 2008).
2. Joint United Nations Programme on HIV/AIDS and World Health Organization, *AIDS Epidemic Update 2007* (Geneva: 2007).
3. Ibid.
4. U.N. Population Division, *Trends in Total Migrant Stock, The 2005 Revision* (New York: 2006).
5. U.N. Population Division director Hania Zlotnik, quoted in U.N. Department of Public Information, Press Conference on International Migration and Development, press release (New York: 4 April 2006).
6. U.N. Population Division, Department of Economic and Social Affairs, *World Urbanization Prospects 2007* (New York: 2008).
7. Population size from U.S. Census Bureau, U.S. POP-Clock Projection, available at www.census.gov/population/www/popclockus.html, viewed 29 January 2008; fertility rate from Population Division, op. cit. note 1.
8. Brady E. Hamilton, Joyce A. Martin, and Stephanie Ventura, "Births: Preliminary Data for 2006," *National Vital Statistics Reports*, 5 December 2007, pp. 1–18.
9. Susheela Singh et al., *Adding It Up: The Benefits of Investing in Sexual and Reproductive Health Care* (New York: Alan Guttmacher Institute, 2003).
10. J. Joseph Speidel, "Population Donor Landscape Analysis for Review of Packard Foundation International Grantmaking in Population, Sexual and Reproductive Health and Rights," Presented at task force of The David and Lucile Packard Foundation, Los Altos, CA, 6 September 2006.
11. Ricardo Hausmann, Laura D. Tyson, and Saadia Zahidi, *The WEF Global Gender Gap Report 2007* (Geneva: World Economic Forum, 2007).
12. Ibid.

CHILD MORTALITY DROPS BELOW 10 MILLION (pages 86–88)

1. United Nations Children's Fund (UNICEF), *The State of the World's Children 2008* (New York: 2007), p. 6.
2. Ibid.

3. Diane Alarcón and Marcos Robles, "The Challenges of Measuring Child Mortality when Birth Registration Is Incomplete," U.N. Department of Economic and Social Affairs, Global Forum on Gender Statistics, Rome, 10–12 December 2007.
4. UNICEF, *Progress for Children: A World Fit for Children—Statistical Review* (New York: 2007), p. 19.
5. Ibid.
6. Ibid.
7. Ibid.
8. Ibid., p. 18.
9. Ibid.
10. UNICEF, op. cit. note 1, p. 6.
11. Ibid., p. 150.
12. U.N. Economic Commission for Latin America and the Caribbean, *The Millennium Development Goals: A Latin American and Caribbean Perspective* (Santiago, Chile: 2005), p. 140.
13. Ibid.
14. UNICEF, op. cit. note 1, p. 7.
15. Ibid.
16. UNICEF, *Progress for Children: A Report Card on Nutrition* (New York: 2006).
17. U.N. Population Division, *World Population Prospects: The 2006 Revision* (New York: 2007).
18. UNICEF, "Child Deaths Fall below 10 Million for First Time," press release (New York: 13 September 2007).
19. UNICEF, op. cit. note 1, p. 7.
20. Ibid.
21. U.N. Population Division, op. cit. note 17.
22. UNICEF, op. cit. note 1, p. 7.
23. Robert E. Black, Saul S. Morris, and Jennifer Bryce, "Where and Why Are 10 Million Children Dying Every Year?" *The Lancet*, 28 June 2003, pp. 226–34; World Health Organization (WHO), *The World Health Report 2005* (Geneva: 2005), Annex Table, pp. 190–91.
24. UNICEF, *Progress for Children: A Report Card on Water and Sanitation* (New York: 2006), p. 3.
25. UNICEF, op. cit. note 1, p. 15.
26. UNICEF, op. cit. note 4, p. 22.
27. Ibid.
28. Ibid., p. 24.
29. WHO, op. cit. note 23, p. 9.
30. Ibid., p. 10.
31. Ibid., p. 83.
32. UNICEF, op. cit. note 4, p. 25.
33. UNICEF, op. cit. note 16; UNICEF, op. cit. note 4, p. 19.

34. UNICEF, op. cit. note 1.

35. Countdown Coverage Writing Group, "Countdown to 2015 for Maternal, Newborn, and Child Survival: The 2008 Report on Tracking Coverage of Interventions," *The Lancet*, 12 April 2008, pp. 1247–58.

36. M. Claeson et al., "Reducing Child Mortality in India in the New Millennium," *Bulletin of the World Health Organization*, October 2000, pp. 1192–99.

37. UNICEF, op. cit. note 1, p. 20.

38. Pan American Health Organization, *Exclusion in Health in Latin America and the Caribbean* (Washington, DC: 2004).

39. UNICEF, op. cit. note 1, p. 20.

40. U.N. Population Division, op. cit. note 17.

41. UNICEF, *Africa's Orphaned and Vulnerable Generation: Children Affected by AIDS* (New York: 2006).

42. UNICEF, op. cit. note 4, p. 19.

43. UNICEF, *Progress for Children: A Child Survival Report Card* (New York: 2004).

44. UNICEF, op. cit. note 18.

45. UNICEF, op. cit. note 4, pp. 19, 21.

46. UNICEF, op. cit. note 1, p. 1.

ENVIRONMENT A GROWING DRIVER IN DISPLACEMENT OF PEOPLE (pages 89–91)

1. Total of 184 million based on U.N. High Commissioner for Refugees (UNHCR), *2007 Global Trends: Refugees, Asylum-seekers, Returnees, Internally-Displaced and Stateless Persons* (Geneva: 2008), p. 2, on Internal Displacement Monitoring Centre (IDMC), *Internal Displacement. Global Overview of Trends and Development in 2007* (Geneva: 2008), p. 7, and on Christian Aid, *Human Tide: The Real Migration Crisis* (London: May 2007), p. 5; Brazil comparison based on data from Population Reference Bureau, *2007 World Population Data Sheet* (Washington, DC: 2007).

2. UNHCR, op. cit. note 1; IDMC, op. cit. note 1.

3. UNHCR, op. cit. note 1.

4. Ibid.

5. Christian Aid, op. cit. note 1.

6. Steffen Angenendt, "International Migration—Just a Matter of State Security?" in Jerry Sommer and Andrea Warnecke, eds., *The Security-Migration Nexus: Challenges and Opportunities of African Migration to EU Countries* (Bonn, Germany: Bonn International Center for Conversion, 2008), p. 19.

7. Ibid.

8. UNHCR, "Annual UNHCR Figures Show Continuing Climb in Number of Uprooted," press release (London: 17 June 2008).

9. Ibid.

10. United Nations Relief and Works Agency for Palestine Refugees in the Near East, "UNRWA Publications/Statistics," at www.unrwa.org, viewed 23 June 2008.

11. IDMC, op. cit. note 1, p. 6.

12. Julian Borger, "Conflicts Fuelled by Climate Change Causing Refugee Crisis, Warns UN," (London) *The Guardian*, 17 June 2008.

13. Fabrice Renaud et al., *Control, Adapt or Flee: How to Face Environmental Migration?* InterSecTions No. 5/2007 (Bonn, Germany: United Nations University Institute for Environment and Human Security UNU-EHS, 2007), p. 10.

14. Essam El-Hinnawi, *Environmental Refugees* (Nairobi: United Nations Environment Programme, 1985).

15. Rhoda Margesson, "Environmental Refugees," in Worldwatch Institute, *State of the World 2005* (New York: W. W. Norton & Company, 2005), p. 40.

16. Christian Aid, op. cit. note 1, p. 6.

17. According to the 1951 United Nations Convention Relating to the Status of Refugees, a refugee is defined as someone who "owing to well-founded fear of being persecuted for reasons of race, religion, nationality, membership of a particular social group or political opinion, is outside the country of his nationality and is unable, or owing to such fear, is unwilling to avail himself of the protection of that country; or who, not having a nationality and being outside the country of his former habitual residence as a result of such events, is unable or, owing to such fear, is unwilling to return to it." See UNHCR, *Convention and Protocol Relating to the Status of Refugees* (Geneva: 2007), p. 16.

18. Vikram Odedra Kolmannskog, *Future Flood of Refugees. A Comment on Climate Change, Conflict and Forced Migration* (Oslo: Norwegian Refugee Council, 2008), p. 9.

19. German Advisory Council on Global Change, *Climate Change as a Security Risk* (London: Earthscan, 2008).

20. Renaud et al., op. cit. note 13.

21. Kolmannskog, op. cit. note 18, p. 16.

22. Renaud et al., op. cit. note 13, p. 27.

23. Masud Karim, "Bangladesh Faces Climate Change Refugee Nightmare," *Reuters*, 14 April 2008.

24. Ibid.

25. Renaud et al., op. cit. note 13, p. 22.

26. Simon Gardner, "Leader of Imperiled Maldives Issues Stark Warning on Sea Level Rise," *International Herald Tribune*, 4 February 2007; John R. Hunter, *A Note on Relative Sea Level Change at Funafuti, Tuvalu* (Hobart, Australia: Antarctic Cooperative Research Centre, 18 August 2002).

27. Renaud et al., op. cit. note 13, p. 24.

28. "The Almeria Statement on Desertification and Migration," International Symposium on Desertification and Migrations, Almeria, Spain, 9–11 February 1994, at www.unccd.int/regional/northmed/meet ings/others/1994AlmeriaSpain.pdf.

29. Oli Brown, "Climate Change and Forced Migrations: Observations, Projections and Implications," Background Paper for U.N. Development Programme (UNDP), *Human Development Report 2007/2008*, p. 11.

30. Kolmannskog, op. cit. note 18, p. 15.

31. Ibid., p. 13; Brown, op. cit. note 29, p. 15.

32. Brown, op. cit. note 29, p. 13.

33. UNDP, *Human Development Report 2007/2008* (New York: Palgrave Macmillan, 2007), p. 189.

The Vital Signs Series

Some topics are included each year in *Vital Signs*; others are covered only in certain years. The following is a list of topics covered in *Vital Signs* thus far, with the year or years they appeared indicated in parentheses. The reference to 2006 indicates *Vital Signs 2006–2007*; 2007 refers to *Vital Signs 2007–2008*.

ENERGY & TRANSPORTATION

Fossil Fuels
    Carbon Use (1993)
    Coal (1993–96, 1998, 2009)
    Fossil Fuels Combined (1997, 1999–2003, 2005–07)
    Natural Gas (1992, 1994–96, 1998)
    Oil (1992–96, 1998, 2009)
Renewables, Efficiency, Other Sources
    Biofuels (2005–07, 2009)
    Biomass Energy (1999)
    Combined Heat and Power (2009)
    Compact Fluorescent Lamps (1993–96, 1998–2000, 2002, 2009)
    Efficiency (1992, 2002, 2006)
    Geothermal Power (1993, 1997)
    Hydroelectric Power (1993, 1998, 2006)
    Nuclear Power (1992–2003, 2005–07, 2009)
    Solar Cells (1992–2002, 2005–07, 2009)
    Wind Power (1992–2003, 2005–07, 2009)
Transportation
    Air Travel (1993, 1999, 2005–07)
    Bicycles (1992–2003, 2005–07, 2009)
    Car-sharing (2002, 2006)

Electric Cars (1997)
Gas Prices (2001)
Motorbikes (1998)
Railroads (2002)
Urban Transportation (1999, 2001)
Vehicles (1992–2003, 2005–07, 2009)

ENVIRONMENT & CLIMATE

Atmosphere and Climate
    Carbon Emissions (1992, 1994–2002, 2009)
    Carbon and Temperature Combined (2003, 2005–07, 2009)
    CFC Production (1992–96, 1998, 2002)
    Global Temperature (1992–2002)
    Ozone Layer (1997, 2007)
    Sea Level Rise (2003)
    Weather-related Disasters (1996–2001, 2003, 2005–07, 2009)
Natural Resources, Animals, Plants
    Amphibians (1995, 2000)
    Aquatic Species (1996, 2002)
    Birds (1992, 1994, 2001, 2003, 2006)
    Coral Reefs (1994, 2001, 2006)
    Dams (1995)

Ecosystem Conversion (1997)
Energy Productivity (1994)
Forests (1992, 1994–98, 2002, 2005–06)
Groundwater (2000, 2006)
Ice Melting (2000, 2005)
Invasive Species (2007)
Mammals (2005)
Mangroves (2006)
Marine Mammals (1993)
Organic Waste Reuse (1998)
Plant Diversity (2006)
Primates (1997)
Terrestrial Biodiversity (2007)
Threatened Species (2007)
Tree Plantations (1998)
Vertebrates (1998)
Water Scarcity (1993, 2001–02)
Water Tables (1995, 2000)
Wetlands (2001, 2005)
Pollution
Acid Rain (1998)
Air Pollution (1993, 1999, 2005)
Algal Blooms (1999)
Hazardous Wastes (2002)
Lead in Gasoline (1995)
Mercury (2006)
Nuclear Waste (1992, 1995)
Ocean (2007)
Oil Spills (2002)
Pollution Control Markets (1998)
Sulfur and Nitrogen Emissions (1994–97)
Other Environmental Topics
Bottled Water (2007)
Environmental Indicators (2006)
Environmental Treaties (1995, 1996, 2000, 2002)
Semiconductor Impacts (2002)
Transboundary Parks (2002)
World Heritage Sites (2003)

FOOD & AGRICULTURE

Agriculture
Farmland Quality (2002)

Fertilizer Use (1992–2001)
Genetically Modified Crops (1999–2002, 2009)
Grain Area (1992–93, 1996–97, 1999–2000)
Grain Production (1994–95, 1998, 2009)
Irrigation (1992, 1994, 1996–99, 2002, 2007)
Nitrogen Fixation (1998)
Organic Agriculture (1996, 2000)
Pesticide Control or Trade (1996, 2000, 2002, 2006)
Pesticide Resistance (1994, 1999)
Soil Erosion (1992, 1995)
Urban Agriculture (1997)
Food Trends
Aquaculture (1994, 1996, 1998, 2002, 2005)
Aquaculture and Fish Combined (2006–07, 2009)
Cocoa Production (2002)
Coffee (2001)
Eggs (2007)
Fish Harvest (1992–2000)
Grain Production (1992–2003, 2005–07)
Grain Stocks (1992–99)
Grain Used for Feed (1993, 1995–96)
Livestock (2001)
Meat (1992–2000, 2003, 2005–07, 2009)
Milk (2001)
Soybeans (1992–2001, 2007)
Sugar and Sweetener Use (2002)

GLOBAL ECONOMY & RESOURCES

Resource Economics
Agricultural Subsidies (2003)
Aluminum (2001, 2006–07)
Arms and Grain Trade (1992)
Commodity Prices (2001)
Fossil Fuel Subsidies (1998)
Gold (1994, 2000, 2007)
Illegal Drugs (2003)
Metals Exploration (1998, 2002)

POPULATION & SOCIETY

Soda Consumption (2002)
Traffic Accidents (1994)
Tuberculosis (2000)
Military
  Armed Forces (1997)
  Arms Production (1997)
  Arms Trade (1994)
  Landmines (1996, 2002)
  Military Expenditures (1992, 1998, 2003, 2005–06)
  Nuclear Arsenal (1992–96, 1999, 2001, 2005, 2007)
  Peacekeeping Expenditures (1994–2003, 2005–07, 2009)
  Resource Wars (2003)
  Wars (1995, 1998–2003, 2005–07)
  Small Arms (1998–99)
Reproductive Health and Women's Status
  Family Planning Access (1992)
  Female Education (1998)
  Fertility Rates (1993)
  Maternal Mortality (1992, 1997, 2003)
  Population Growth (1992–2003, 2005–07, 2009)
  Sperm Count (1999, 2007)
  Violence Against Women (1996, 2002)
  Women in Politics (1995, 2000)

Social Inequities
  Homelessness (1995)
  Income Distribution (1992, 1995, 1997, 2002–03)
  Language Extinction (1997, 2001, 2006)
  Literacy (1993, 2001, 2007)
  Prison Populations (2000)
  Slums (2006)
  Social Security (2001)
  Teacher Supply (2002)
  Unemployment (1999, 2005)
Other Social Topics
  Aging Populations (1997)
  Environmental Refugees (2009)
  Fast-Food Use (1999)
  International Criminal Court (2003)
  Millennium Development Goals (2005, 2007)
  Nongovernmental Organizations (1999)
  Orphans Due to AIDS Deaths (2003)
  Public Policy Networks (2005)
  Quality of Life (2006)
  Refugees (1993–2000, 2001, 2003, 2005)
  Religious Environmentalism (2001)
  Sustainable Communities (2007)
  Urbanization (1995–96, 1998, 2000, 2002, 2007)
  Voter Turnouts (1996, 2002)

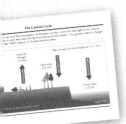
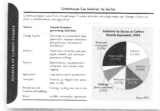

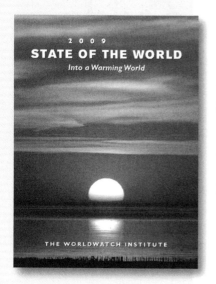

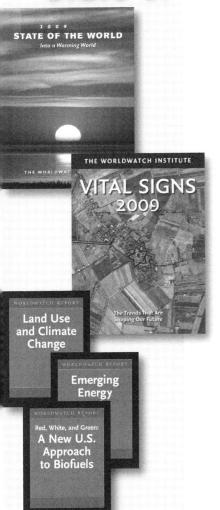

Announcing Vital Signs Online

Vital Signs Online provides more than 30 sustainability trends with hard data and research-based insights for each trend that **you can't find anywhere else**. In one place, you'll have trend data over multiple decades along with concise and thoughtful analysis of the most critical global trends needed by business leaders, policymakers, journalists, strategists, students, and engaged citizens.

With an annual subscription to Vital Signs Online you'll get:

- Unlimited access to more than 30 sustainability trends in five categories: Food & Agriculture; Energy & Transportation; Environment & Climate; Global Economy & Resources; and Population & Society

- Worldwatch's highly respected, clear analysis for each trend

- Presentation-ready charts and graphs that can be customized

- Excel spreadsheets that allow data manipulation for instructional and comparative purposes according to personal or organizational needs

- Full endnote referencing

> *"Vital Signs…provides the most straightforward and reliable environmental, economic, and social information available on the entire planet Earth. Vital Signs delivers…facts illuminated by contexts and interconnections, often revealing causes of the problems, and pointing the way towards solutions that work."*
> —**Michael Pastore, Editorial Director, Epublishers Weekly**

**From the boardroom to the classroom,
Vital Signs Online will be your reliable tool for bringing
your research or presentation to the next level.**

Worldwatch is slated to launch this new subscription service by mid-2009. Check our website for availability of the trends online or sign up for our Vital Signs Alerts by going to www.worldwatch.org/email_signup.

Worldwatch Reports